HUMAN HEREDITY

HUMAN HEREDITY

by JEAN ROSTAND

PHILOSOPHICAL LIBRARY

New York

Translated from the French L'Hérédité Humaine
by WADE BASKIN

FOREWORD

For more than a quarter of a century Dr. Jean Rostand has been absorbed in the study of hereditary and acquired anomalies. He speaks with authority on a wide range of subjects and has pioneered in research directed toward establishing laboratory techniques for controlling and modifying genetic processes. Like many of his colleagues, he has contributed significantly to the advancement of science by conducting exhaustive research within his field of specialization—in his case, parthenogenesis in batrachians. Unlike many of his colleagues, however, he has long recognized the significance of popularization in science and has written intelligently about complex issues in which the general public has a vested interest. For his efforts to "introduce the greatest number of people into the sovereign dignity of knowledge," he has won international acclaim.

The words just quoted, one part of his definition of popularization, are taken from an address recently delivered on the occasion of his acceptance of the 1959 Kalinga Prize for "outstanding contributions to the dissemination of scientific knowledge to the general public." His efforts reflect both his concern over the awesome role of science in the modern world and his awareness of the scientist's responsibility to society.

More than fifty volumes, mainly on scientific and technical subjects, have resulted from Dr. Rostand's investigations and reflections. Unfortunately, readers on this side of the Atlantic have had access to only three of his works: *Adventures before Birth* (Ryerson, 1936); *Life, the Great Adventure* (Scribner's, 1956); and *Can Man Be Modified?* (Basic Books, 1959). As the titles suggest, his enthusiasm for the pursuit of knowledge never wanes, but his guarded optimism is tempered always by his concern over the uses to which individuals or nations may put the results of scientific discoveries.

Dr. Rostand is known to the American public mainly through journalistic accounts of his studies of virgin births among frogs and of his statements concerning the moral implications of recent developments in genetics. For example, his studies of fatherless frogs have enabled him to posit fatherless—and even motherless—children. Staggering indeed are the philosophical and moral problems that would of necessity arise in a society of artificially conceived offspring.

Son of the celebrated author of *Cyrano de Bergerac* and brother of another reputable dramatist, Dr. Rostand has earned many citations and awards, both literary and scientific. The present work evidences his sure grasp of the basic facts of human heredity and—in the French version, at any rate—his talent as a writer. More than this, it reveals him as a humanitarian deeply disturbed by the philosophical and moral implications of scientific intervention in the process of reproduction.

I am glad to have had a hand in making available to the English-speaking public this timely work on an issue in which each of us has a vested interest. Explanatory notes, unless otherwise specified, are to be attributed to the author. For the convenience of readers, English titles have been substituted for the French works listed by Dr. Rostand in footnotes and at the end of the last chapter.

To all those who shared with me the joys and pains entailed by our task, a word of appreciation is in order: to Dr. Wayne Silver, Professor of Biological Science, who read the translation in its entirety and offered many constructive suggestions; to Dr. Leslie Dwight, Professor of Mathematics, and to Arnold Walker, Instructor in Physical Science, who clarified certain technical points; and to Amy Aston, Robert Burton, Whulen Cox, Edyth Ebel, Joe Fox, Betty Swearengin, and Joe Vaughan, who contributed in their several ways to the completion of the undertaking. For any inaccuracies or shortcomings, I alone am responsible.

Southeastern State College   Wade Baskin

CONTENTS

HUMAN HEREDITY

Chapter I

HEREDITY

It is customary in speaking of human heredity to recall the famous passage from Book II of Montaigne's *Essays:*

> How strange that the drop of semen from which we spring bears in itself the impression not only of the bodily shape but also of the thoughts and inclinations of our fathers! Where does that drop of fluid harbor such an infinite number of forms? And how do they convey those resemblances, so bold and unpredictable in their course that the great-grandson will be like his great-grandfather and the nephew like his uncle?

Indeed, this passage, which dates from the sixteenth century, is in every respect remarkable. It poses not only the problem of the transmission of physical characters or somatic heredity but also that of psychic heredity; it calls attention to the apparently capricious or unpredictable nature of this transmission; and, most important, it expresses vividly the surprise and bewilderment of a mind confronted by the great phenomenon of heredity.

More than four hundred years have passed since it was written, and we obviously know now much more than Montaigne about the mechanism and principles that relate to the transmission of characters; but in spite of the progress of our science, we are still impressed, and no less vividly than the author of the *Essays*, when we consider the great number of things, both physical and moral, contained in the minute seed responsible for the birth of a human being. Our astonishment today is simply predicated on more facts and a better understanding of heredity than was then possible. We know that the human being is not produced by a drop of semen but by a *zygote*, that is, by a *cell* or minute vesicle of living matter, and that the formation of the zygote—the sole link between generations—requires the co-opera-tion of two distinct cells, each from a different source.

These two cells—called *sex cells, reproductive cells*, or *gametes*—are emitted, respectively, by two individual parents: one of them, the *egg* or the *ovule*, by the mother; and the other, the *sperm* or the *spermatozoon*, by the father (Fig. 1).

Here it is impossible to describe in detail the structure and constitution of these cells. We know that in them must be sought the origin of all heredi-tary resemblances and of all likenesses between pro-creator and procreated, between the parent and the child. For the moment, however, we need only ob-serve that the two reproductive cells differ strikingly, both in size and in shape.

The male cell, equipped with a long tail or flagel-lum, looks remarkably slender in comparison with the spherical female cell. Whereas the ovule is barely visible to the naked eye (0.2 millimeter in diameter),

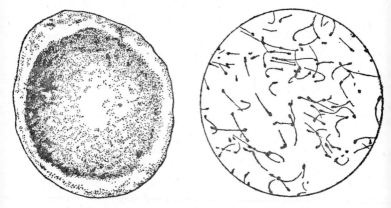

Fig. 1 Human ovule and Spermatozoa
(After Scheinfeld)

the spermatozoon is only 0.07 millimeter (or 70 *micra*) long and can be seen only with the aid of a powerful microscope. Its size is only 1/500 that of the ovum.

The ovule is perfectly motionless; a woman produces but one each month. Spermatozoa are extremely active; they swim rapidly through the seminal fluid, like tadpoles in water; a small drop of semen probably contains several million of them.

Following coition, a single spermatozoon penetrates and fertilizes the ovule. Shortly after fertilization has occurred, the ovule—which has become a zygote—divides into two cells, each of which divides into two more cells, and so on until through a series of such bipartitions trillions of cells are formed, constituting the body of the new individual.

This cursory review of a few elementary concepts shows that the problem of heredity is reduced in the final analysis to a cellular problem.[1] If a child resembles his parents, this is because he owes his origin to a cell resulting from a joint contribution made by his father and his mother: the union of a paternal cell and a maternal cell.

The zygote is not an ordinary, commonplace cell, for it is capable of producing a complete individual. But here we cannot take up the problem of the nature of the zygote, which is the central problem in embryology. In the present work we are concerned with another problem: Why does the zygote necessarily produce an individual with traits similar to those of its parents? We begin by trying to define more precisely the notion of *germinal* or *hereditary determination*.

One does not have to be a biologist to know that human zygotes will produce only human beings, just as canine zygotes will produce only dogs, and just as zygotes from whales will produce only whales.

On this point heredity defies any infraction of the rule: *Specific heredity* is absolute, at least under present conditions of relative fixity of living species. One individual can never give birth to another individual belonging to a different species.

Clearly defined racial characters follow a similar pattern. From a zygote produced by a Negro man and a Negro woman can come only a Negro child. From a zygote produced by a white man and a white woman can come only a white child. There is no possible exception to this rule of *racial heredity*.

Nor does one have to be a biologist to know that heredity is not merely specific or racial but also individual in the sense that it determines characters and traits peculiar to certain individuals. As a matter of fact, this is the sort of heredity that the layman generally has in mind when he speaks of human heredity. He generally thinks of the resemblance between children and their parents, grandparents, collateral ancestors, etc.

To be sure, no one is surprised if a child has his father's nose, or his mother's or his grandfather's eyes, or even if there is but a vague resemblance between the child and his ancestors. In the transmission of individual characters there are no absolute rules such as those that determine specific or racial heredity. Later this apparently capricious element in individual heredity will be explained. For the moment we merely call attention to the fact—to be dealt with subsequently at greater length—that many individual characters are already imprinted on the fertilized egg, and that during this early stage are determined not only its species but also its individuality.

In the human zygote there exists not only a potential human being but also a particular human being with eyes of a certain color, with hair of a certain shade, with certain facial features, with blood of a certain type, etc.

The power of heredity to determine individual characters shows up clearly in the study of *human twins*.

There are two types of twins, or individuals born of the same pregnancy.

Sometimes they come from *two distinct zygotes,* produced simultaneously by the mother and fertilized independently of each other. In such cases they are *fraternal twins*—in reality simply brothers or sisters who have developed side by side in the same matrix. They resemble each other no more closely than do ordinary brothers or sisters.

Identical twins, on the other hand, come from a single fertilized egg which splits in two at the beginning of its development and produces two distinct individuals.[2] Identical twins, who have the same origin and consequently the same genetic endowment, are amazingly alike. They are always of the same sex, and have the same eyes, the same hair, the same facial features, the same shape of eye-brows, the same folds in the lingual mucosa, the same blood characters;[3] they resemble each other down to the imprints made by their palms and fingers—details which are generally sufficiently distinctive for legal identification (fingerprint system).[4]

True organic "doubles," identical twins are—according to the apt expression coined by Dr. Alpert— "two copies of the same individual."

Their extraordinary resemblance makes it hard to tell them apart and thus gives rise to misunderstandings. This accounts for the frequent use of identical twins in dramatic literature, ranging from Plautus' *The Menaechmi Twins* to Tristan Bernard's plays.

Professor Newman of Chicago, a specialist in the study of twins, has cited some striking facts concerning identical twins who were separated at birth and knew nothing of each other's existence until their physical likeness caused them to be brought together again as adults.

Edwin and Fred, for instance, lived nine hundred miles apart. At twenty-two, Edwin, passing by chance through the town in which Fred was living, was approached on the street by a person who called him Fred. Astonished, he replied that his name was not Fred; his interlocutor was persistent and finally made him understand that he had been mistaken for a twin whose existence was first revealed to him through this encounter.

Or take a case cited by Vandel. Two conductors, Wolf and Will Heinz, could substitute for each other during a performance, undetected by either the audience or the musicians; a film revealed that their technical movements were identical.

Naturally, we must not carry things too far and pretend, as people sometimes do, that identical twins are alike with respect to intelligence, character, tastes, and behavior, that they think about the same things at the same time, etc. Especially when twins are separated at birth and accordingly exposed to different environmental and educational conditions, marked differences may result, at least from the intellectual and the moral viewpoint. And one of the main advantages in the study of twins is that it helps us to distinguish between the role of *heredity* and that of environment in the formation of the human personality.

Chapter II

HEREDITY AND ENVIRONMENT

We have just seen that there is, in addition to specific heredity and racial heredity, individual heredity in the sense that the human zygote is at the outset strongly individualized and personalized. In many respects the human being is predetermined at conception. This conclusion is inescapable in view of the extraordinary physical resemblance or quasi-identity of individuals born of the same zygote (identical twins). Nevertheless, to avoid grave misunderstandings, we should understand clearly that the individual is predetermined at conception only *potentially*.

The zygote contains no part of the individual, no trace of a rudimentary organ. Nor could the most powerful microscope reveal anything even resembling the shape or features of a man.

For example, we have seen that eye color is determined at conception; still, the zygote contains neither a human eye, nor the outline of a human eye, nor anything that could possibly be said to develop into an eye or contribute to the formation of an eye. All that we know is that the zygote contains certain materials, certain substances whose nature or arrangement are such that when the eye is formed during the developmental process, it will take on a certain color. Between the *initial* stage of the zygote and the *final* stage of the individual equipped with brown or blue eyes is a whole series of complex events—chemical reactions, we might say—about which we now know practically nothing. The same holds true for every other character and for every other part of the organism. It is assumed, however, that during the long formative or *developmental* period bridging germinal potentialities and the realization of physical characters, external factors (*environment*) can intervene and exert a strong influence on the formation of the individual. That is why the term germinal determination, which we have used up to this point, might lead to confusion unless satisfactorily defined.

In the case of human beings, first comes the *maternal environment* in which the embryo develops, then, after birth, the *external environment*.

It is important to note that the role played by the environment in shaping characters varies considerably according to the character studied.

For instance, we know of practically no condition capable of modifying eye color. Theoretically, there is nothing to rule out the possibility of the discovery of an artificial means of influencing eye color, but within the frame of our present state of knowledge, we can state that when a human zygote receives a certain genetic endowment, it unfailingly produces an individual with eyes of a certain color. Eye color is then irrevocably determined at conception, as are many other characters still to be considered: facial features, blood group, etc.

Here environmental conditions have absolutely no effect; heredity is everything. But in addition to such cases, which are clearly defined and which brook no reservations, we find many characters on which environment—either maternal or external—exerts an influence which is far from negligible.

Take pigmentation of the skin: the degree of pigmentation will vary with the intensity of the solar rays to which the skin is exposed, that is, with the climate of the region in which the individual lives.

Size will depend not only on hereditary factors but also on the amount of food ingested during the early years that comprise the period of growth. That is why, statistically, members of the working classes, badly nourished, are somewhat smaller than members of the wealthy classes. To the extent that size also depends on hormones, notably those secreted by the thyroid gland and the pituitary gland, it can be modified by the effect of a disease affecting the endocrine glands. Of two identical twins (who ought to be the same size in terms of their heredity), one may be much smaller than the other as a result of an infection contracted during childhood.

Investigations carried out in different countries relating to immigrant populations suggest that the shape and size of the head, and even the nasal index, are modified to some degree by external influences (Boas, Shapiro). The shape of a child's head, in particular, can be modified by the softness or hardness of his crib, by the amount of vitamins in his diet, etc.

A grave affection causing physical and moral retardation—*Mongolian idiocy*—provides a good example of the combined effects of heredity and environment.[1]

Today it has been established that this defect depends on hereditary factors in the sense that no external circumstance is capable of producing it if the zygote does not carry a certain genetic substance. Against this, it has also been established that the genetic substance produces its effect much more frequently when the foetus is carried by an aged mother. Statistics show that the greatest number of Mongolian children are born to mothers approaching the age of forty.[2]

If we pass from the physical side of the individual to his intellectual and moral qualities, which are formed slowly, belatedly, and with the constant concurrence of educational and social stimulations, we must reckon to an even greater degree with the role of environment. We shall return to this capital point in dealing with the inheritance of intelligence and special aptitudes.

It follows that there is no basis for contrasting (as people too often do) *heredity* and *environment,* or *nature* and *nurture,* to use the expressions that have gained currency in English. Both factors contribute essentially to the formation of the individual. They work closely together, fusing their efforts to the point where it is often difficult to discriminate between the contribution made by one and that made by the other. Discrimination is further complicated by the fact that two individuals—unless they are identical twins who have the same heredity—always differ both as to germinal origin and as to the circumstances of their development. Just as each man, as we shall see, owes his origin to a particular zygote, he develops in a particular environment. Human beings differ no less on account of their life history than on account of their origin.

Finally, it should be noted that, according to some

authorities, hereditary determinism and circumstantial determinism together would not suffice to explain the total formation of the human being. Thus, if we wished to be extremely circumspect, we might, along with the biologist J. B. S. Haldane, reserve a blank space or an X for those human differences that might be attributable to causes other than environment and heredity: According to Haldane,

> If there is such a thing as free will in the most profound sense, it comes under the rubric X. I consider it unscientific to exclude X, if only for this reason: If there is no X, if all differences between human beings are rigidly determined, then it will be possible in a few centuries to prove that in certain areas at least 99.9%, say, of these differences are determined by differences in nature or in nurture. As I see it, it is better to prove that 99.9% are so determined than to affirm *a priori* that 100% are. If we then leave X in our scheme, we can say that in certain cases, such as skin color, X is certainly weak; and in the case of a difference in behavior, we can hope, depending on our overall philosophy, that X is either very negligible or very important.[3]

Chapter III

CHROMOSOMES

To advance our analysis of the phenomenon of human heredity we must again consider the germ cell, which is responsible for any similarity between parent and offspring.

Each reproductive cell, whether that of the male (spermatozoon) or that of the female (ovule), contains a slightly denser portion called the *nucleus* [1]; in the nucleus are distinct particles which are called *chromosomes* because they readily absorb certain stains used in the laboratory to make specimens visible under the microscope.

The number of chromosomes is constant in every cell in the same individual and in every individual belonging to the same species. In each human germ cell (spermatozoon or ovule) there are twenty-four chromosomes of diverse shapes and sizes; each chromosome in the ovule is matched by one in the spermatozoon.

The fertilized egg therefore contains forty-eight chromosomes, of which twenty-four come from the mother and twenty-four from the father (fig. 2). [2]

The single fact that the chromosomes are found in equal number in the two parent cells that differ so markedly in other respects, when added to the fact that both parents have an equal or almost equal share in the process of transmission, persuades us from the outset to attribute to these particles a basic role in heredity. Furthermore, their role is established by an infinite array of data assembled, not about man, but about animals, chiefly the small vinegar fly or Drosophila, admirably studied by Morgan and his associates.[3]

It has been established beyond doubt that chromosomes play a preponderant role in the transmission of a host of organic characters, for the latter are rigidly controlled by the fate of the former. The mechanism of heredity, as revealed through experimental crossings, is but the mechanism of chromosome distribution. It has also been established beyond doubt that each chromosome is a complex unit whose different

Fig. 2.—The twenty-four pairs of chromosomes. (After Evans and Swezy.)

particles play distinct roles in the transmission of characters. In both animals and plants it has been possible to advance the analysis of the basic stuff of heredity far enough to determine not only that a certain character depends on a certain chromosome but also that it is associated with a certain region (*locus*) on the chromosome.

In the case of Drosophila—long favored in genetic

experiments—it has been observed, for example, that modification of a minute particle of one of the four chromosomes (Number 1) entails the elimination of pigment in the eye (white-eyed mutation); it has also been observed that in the same chromosome reduplication of a certain segment entails atrophy of the eye, characteristic of bar mutation.

Insofar as the human species is concerned, any thought of collecting such precise data is obviously premature. Man is a poor subject for studies of inheritance, and this for several reasons, not the least of which is the fact that geneticists find it impossible to perform experimental crossings of their congeners. Thanks to the study of genealogies or pedigrees, however, we know the mode of transmission of a large number of characters and can be certain that they are transmitted exactly in accordance with the chromosome theory of heredity.

Before we consider the chromosome theory of heredity, it is necessary for us to observe the chromosomes throughout the life cycle of the human being in order to see how they persist and are transmitted from one generation to the next.

We have just noted that the human zygote contains in the nucleus forty-eight chromosomes of which twenty-four come from the maternal cell and twenty-four from the paternal cell. When at the beginning of its embryonic development the fertilized egg divides into two daughter cells, each chromosome also splits longitudinally and contributes one of its threads to each daughter cell.[4] This process is repeated for all subsequent divisions, with the result that in each of the cells that constitute the organism, there will be

forty-eight chromosomes, each one identical in composition to the original chromosome of which it is the
direct descendant.

Now in the formation of mature germ cells—
either ova or spermatozoa—one of the cell divisions
that precedes their genesis exhibits a distinctive trait:
instead of receiving *all* its chromosomes according to
the usual pattern of cell division, it receives only half,
or twenty-four—one chromosome out of two, one of
each kind, one of each pair—and in each instance this
may be either the paternal or the maternal chromosome.

This phenomenon, of extreme importance in understanding the facts of heredity, has been given the
name of *reduction division.*

Reduction division is so important that we need
to dwell on it at some length.

When during chromatic reduction one chromosome from each pair of parental chromosomes enters
the germ cell, *chance* alone determines the selection
of one or the other of the two chromosomes. Here of
course the word chance is not used, as is frequently
the case among philosophers, to mean contingency, or
freedom, or the absence of causation. We certainly
do not mean that a chromosome is free to enter or
not to enter a cell, but only that the forces responsible for the selection of a particular member of the
pair of chromosomes are so tenuous and complex as
to defy any attempt to analyze them, and that it is
impossible to predict what will happen in a particular
case.

It is in exactly the same sense that we say, in the
case of a coin tossed into the air, that *chance* determines whether a head or a tail appears when it falls.[5]

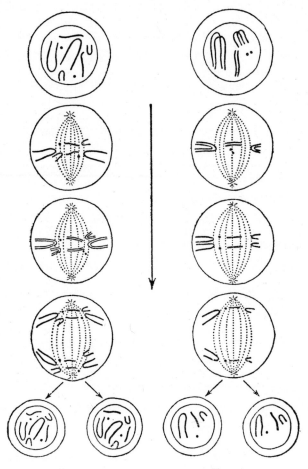

Fig. 3
Ordinary division,
or *mitosis*

Fig. 4
Reduction division,
or *meiosis*

It is obvious that the manner in which the coin falls is determined by the movement of the one who tosses it into the air, by the resistance of the air, etc.; no matter how rigid its causal determinism, the phenomenon is much too complex to lend itself to analysis, and we are therefore unable to predict the final result.

To come back to human chromosomes, then, chance determines whether the maternal or the paternal chromosome in each pair will enter a given germ cell; moreover, during the maturation of the cell, everything happens as if each of its chromosomes were selected by the toss of a coin. And since it receives twenty-four chromosomes, its composition is obviously dependent on twenty-four random assortments.

Furthermore, the twenty-four random assortments are independent of each other since the different pairs of chromosomes are *independent,* and nothing compels chromosomes from the same source (maternal or paternal) to enter the same cell together.

It is of course not impossible for a germ cell to receive *all maternal chromosomes* or *all paternal chromosomes,* but a uniparental distribution is *extremely improbable,* no less so than a distribution of twenty-four heads or twenty-four tails when tossing coins; and this means that the vast majority of germ cells will contain in variable proportions a mixture of the maternal and paternal chromosomes found in the parent.

According to the chromosome theory of heredity each chromosome consists of a set of particles, each with a distinctive role, called *genes.*[6]

A complete complement of genes (*genome*) is necessary for normal development of an organism. The twenty-four chromosomes in the germ cell constitute a genome; the fertilized egg (forty-eight chromosomes) contains two genomes (the genome of maternal origin and the genome of paternal origin), for each gene is represented twice.[7]

Within a species, at any one *locus* (or point on a chromosome), there may be any one of a series of genes (*alleles*) governing a specific character. Hereditary diversity depends on such genic differences.

Certain hereditary differences result from the combined action of multiple differential genes, while others result from the action of but *one differential gene;* the mode of transmission of the latter, called *Mendelian* characters,[8] is quite simple, as will be seen in the next chapter.

Individuals with differential genes will transmit them intact to successive generations if they belong to the same chromosome pair (*linkage*) but will transmit them independently of each other if they belong to distinct chromosome pairs.

Actually, genes carried on the same chromosome only manifest a *tendency* to remain united; in other words, their linkage is not *total*, for frequently during the maturation of the gametes genes are exchanged between chromosomes (paternal and maternal) of the same pair. For example, if an individual has received from one parent a chromosome carrying the genes *A* and *B* and from the other a chromosome carrying the allelic genes *a* and *b*, his gametes may contain chromosomes with either *A* and *b* or *a* and *B*. This exchange of genes is known as *crossing over*. The

possibility that two genes on the same chromosome
will be separated increases with the distance between
them. Statistical studies of the phenomenon of crossing over have therefore made it possible to locate
the genes in the different chromosomes of Drosophila
and to draw up chromosome maps.

The essential property of the gene is the power of
self-propagation. With each division of the cell, each
gene in each chromosome builds up a duplicate of
itself alongside itself. In all probability, through the
working of some mechanism which is still not clearly
understood and which is at the crux of the phenomenon of assimilation, the gene causes the cell to
produce a duplicate gene, a copy of itself.

But the copying process is not perfect; sometimes
there are mistakes, lapses that entail genetic *mutations* (the formation of alleles somewhat different from
the regular gene).

It is generally agreed that the gene is a large
molecule of a very complex substance called deoxy-
ribonucleoprotein.[9] Rough calculations have indicated
that its size is a few millimicrons (millionths of a millimeter), but it may well be much smaller, for observations made with an electronic microscope by E.
Guyénot and his colleagues suggest that many hypotheses concerning the dimensions of genes, their
nature, and the nature of their mutations will have to
be revised.[10]

The number of genes in man is probably very high
(several tens of thousands). We cannot be more specific than that.

In certain forms of life (Drosophila, Protozoa,
etc.) some racial characters depend on particles found
in the portion of the cell that surrounds the nucleus

(*cytoplasm*); in the human species, however, we have no definite knowledge of any hereditary transmission through the medium of the cytoplasm. All documented cases of racial or individual transmission appear to be based on chromosomal inheritance.[11]

Chapter IV

A MENDELIAN CHARACTER:
EYE COLORATION

In the preceding chapter we indicated the capital role played in the phenomenon of heredity by the particles in the cell nucleus called *chromosomes* and outlined the simple, regular mechanism through which the chromosomes are transmitted from parent to offspring. Now let us consider how knowledge of this mechanism makes possible an understanding of the transmission of hereditary characters.

A number of hereditary characters, as noted previously, exhibit a relatively *simple* mode of transmission because they are determined *by a single gene*.

For example, the difference between brown eyes and blue eyes—a difference attributable to a different distribution of pigment in the iris—relates to the presence in one of the chromosome pairs of a gene which, according to its constitution, causes brown eyes or blue eyes.

A brown-eyed individual with a gene for brown eyes in each member of one particular chromosome pair obviously has *two genes* for brown eyes. Each of his germ cells—it will be recalled that each cell *receives half of his chromosomes and consequently half of his genes*—will receive *one gene* for brown eyes.

Against this, a blue-eyed individual with a gene for blue eyes in each member of the chromosome pair will obviously produce germ cells each containing *one gene* for blue eyes.

In the case of a union between these two individuals (and the result will be the same whether the man is brown-eyed and the woman blue-eyed or vice versa) the child will of necessity inherit a gene for brown eyes from one parent and a gene for blue eyes from the other.

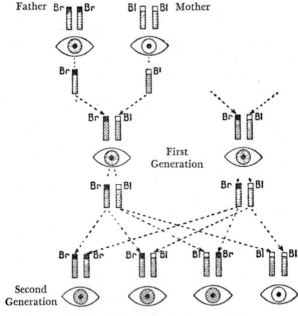

Fig. 5.—Inheritance of eye color
(ordinary heredity)

The child will have brown eyes since the gene for brown eyes dominates the gene for blue eyes; it is a *dominant* gene while the other is a *recessive* one.

All children born of unions of this type are therefore brown-eyed, like their brown-eyed parent. But whereas the parent is *pure* or *homozygous* for the gene for brown eyes, the offspring are *impure* or *heterozygous* since they carry a gene for blue eyes.

We see then that brown-eyed individuals may differ with respect to their genetic constitution: they may or may not carry a hidden gene for blue eyes. In contrast, a blue-eyed individual cannot carry a hidden gene for brown eyes for the reason that if he had in his hereditary endowment the *dominant* gene, he himself would have brown eyes. While brown-eyed individuals may be either homozygous or heterozygous,[1] blue-eyed individuals are homozygous.

What will be the result of a union between a heterozygous brown-eyed individual and a blue-eyed individual?

The homozygous brown-eyed parent will form *two types* of germ cells since any one cell may receive either the chromosome carrying the gene for brown eyes or the chromosome carrying the gene for blue eyes.

And since the blue-eyed parent forms but a single type of germ cell, each containing a chromosome with a gene for blue eyes, there will be born in equal numbers children of *two types:* one type will inherit one gene for brown eyes and one gene for blue eyes while the other will inherit two genes for blue eyes. The first will have brown eyes by virtue of the dominance of brown over blue; the second will have blue eyes.

In this instance *half of the progeny* will have

brown eyes and half blue eyes; in other words, a child will have one chance in two of having either brown eyes or blue eyes.

Naturally, this does not mean that if four children result from such a union, two will have brown eyes and two blue eyes; it means rather that if the total progeny resulting from many such unions is considered, it will be found that approximately half of the children have brown eyes and approximately half have blue eyes. In accordance with the law of averages, the proportion will be more likely to approximate fifty per cent as the number of children increases.

We come finally to the third type of union: that between two heterozygous brown-eyed individuals.

Each parent in this instance forms *two* kinds of germ cells, and in equal number: cells with a gene for brown eyes and cells with a gene for blue eyes.

There are accordingly four possible combinations in the progeny:

(1) When a gamete (sex cell) with a gene for brown eyes fertilizes a gamete with a gene for brown eyes, a brown-eyed individual will result.

(2) When a sperm cell with a gene for brown eyes fertilizes an egg cell with a gene for blue eyes, a brown-eyed individual will result.

(3) When a sperm cell with a gene for blue eyes fertilizes an egg cell with a gene for brown eyes, a brown-eyed individual will result.

(4) Finally, when a gamete with a gene for blue eyes fertilizes a gamete with a gene for blue eyes, a blue-eyed individual will result.

In other words, *three* of the four possible combinations produce brown eyes while *one* produces blue eyes.

In the case of a large number of children resulting from unions of this type it will be found, therefore, that approximately three fourths have brown eyes and one fourth blue.

We note that all the offspring of two blue-eyed individuals will have blue eyes since the parents are necessarily homozygous. Against this, it is impossible to predict with certainty the eye color of the offspring of two brown-eyed individuals. If one of the parents is homozygous, then all the children will have brown eyes; but if both parents are heterozygous, some of their children may be blue-eyed.

We also note that if brown-eyed individuals form unions for several generations, the gene for blue eyes may remain hidden for a long time. It will reappear, or at least may reappear, when there is a union between two individuals who are heterozygous for brown eyes. This explains certain facts about *atavism*.

Everything just said about the inheritance of brown and blue eyes is somewhat oversimplified. This basic scheme of Mendelian inheritance applies to cases in general but may be deficient in exceptional cases, for accessory genes sometimes intervene and complicate the results. In addition, according to Gates, blue is sometimes transmitted as a dominant character.

Chapter V

SIMPLE INHERITANCE

Normal and Slightly Abnormal Characters

We have just examined the inheritance of brown or blue eye coloration. Several human characters show the same type of inheritance: they all depend on *a single chromosomal gene*.

Some of these *Mendelian characters* are normal while others are abnormal. And since the distinction between normality and abnormality is at times arbitrary, we omit in the present chapter everything that has to do with the inheritance of defects and disorders.[1]

Hair color is clearly hereditary. As a rule, dark hair is dominant over light hair. Red hair seems to depend on a special gene, probably one that is recessive.

Curly hair is dominant over straight hair. The investigations of Pruner-Bey indicate that the shape of the hair follicle determines whether the hair is curly or straight; the tube is flat in the case of curly hair and rounded in the case of straight hair.

The Negro's kinky hair is dominant over the White's curly hair, which is in turn dominant over the Melanesian's kinky hair.

Premature greying of the hair is a dominant character, as is the presence of a grey forelock. Harman traced the transmission of the latter character through six consecutive generations.

In certain pedigrees the grey forelock appears only in men even though it is transmitted by women. Later we shall again take up this special mode of inheritance, called sex-linked inheritance (see Chapter VIII).

Premature baldness (occurring before the age of forty-two) depends on a gene whose dominance is effective only in conjunction with a certain hormonal condition (the presence of the male hormone, or *testosterone*). Only rarely are women bald.

The presence or absence of hair on the second or middle digital phalanges is clearly hereditary; it apparently depends on a single gene which, according to Bernstein and Burks, may evince five different states governing as many degrees of digital pilosity.

Passing on to other parts of the body, we note the inheritance of prognathism (dominant), ptosis (dominant), the Mongolian fold in the upper eyelid (dominant in the White-Mongol cross, recessive in the White-Bushman cross), the shape of the nose (the arched nose dominates the flat nose), the thickness of the lips (thick lips dominate thin lips), type of ear lobe (the lobe that hangs free dominates the adherent lobe), etc.

A very special hereditary character, accidentally discovered by Dr. Fox, is the inability to taste a certain chemical substance, phenylthiocarbamide (P. T. C.). One day when the chemical was being prepared in powdered form in his laboratory, Dr. Fox put some of it into a flask, scattering particles in the air as he did so. A laboratory assistant noticed the bitter taste of the powder; but Dr. Fox, though exposed to a larger quantity, had detected no bitterness. Tasting the crystalline substance, he found it insipid while his assistant found it bitter. Other laboratory workers were summoned and invited to taste the substance. Some, like the assistant, found it bitter; others, like Dr. Fox, found it tasteless.

Human beings, then, differ markedly with respect to their ability to taste phenylthiocarbamide.

More recent investigations have shown that the ability or inability to taste various substances is hereditary and that it is transmitted according to Mendelian principles. We now know that the ability to taste P.T.C. is due to a dominant gene while the inability to taste it is due to a recessive gene.

Tasters, as a rule, appreciably outnumber non-tasters.

Similar differences in gustatory sensitivity have been found in apes (chimpanzees) and even in rats.

Chapter VI

BLOOD GROUPS

Among the hereditary characters that have been studied most extensively are those having to do with the composition of the blood. Everyone is aware of the extreme importance acquired in medicine by the notion of blood group first advanced by the illustrious serologist Landsteiner. His discovery has made it possible to avoid today the serious accidents that so frequently happened in former times as a result of transfusions in which the donor's blood was incompatible with the receiver's blood. This incompatibility entailed the agglutination of the donor's blood cells and consequently the production of embolisms, often fatal.

For blood cells to be agglutinated by a serum, they must contain a certain substance called an *agglutinogen;* besides this, the serum must contain another substance capable of causing clumping or agglutination (an *agglutinin*). Now in the human species there are two types of agglutinogens, A and B, matched by two types of agglutinins, anti-A and anti-B. It is obvious that the presence of an agglutinogen in a particular individual's blood cells necessarily excludes the presence of the corresponding agglutinin. Thus blood containing the agglutinogen A does not contain the anti-A agglutinin but instead the anti-B agglutinin; it belongs to group A. In the same way blood containing the agglutinogen B does not contain the anti-B agglutinin but instead the anti-A agglutinin; it belongs to group B. Blood with both agglutinogen A and agglutinogen B contains neither anti-A nor anti-B agglutinin and belongs to group AB. Finally blood with no agglutinogens (neither A nor B) contains both the anti-A and the anti-B agglutinin; it belongs to group O.[1]

Our classification of blood according to four types is an oversimplification of the facts, for certain types are further divided into subgroups.

Noteworthy is the rigidity of the individual's blood type. The group to which the individual belongs can be determined from earliest infancy, and it persists throughout a lifetime. No external influence can modify it, neither infectious diseases, nor vaccinations, nor even blood transfusions. It is strictly hereditary and, as Von Dungern and Hirszfeld showed in 1911, it is a Mendelian character, for it depends on a single chromosomal unit or *gene*.

This gene can appear in *three* different forms, designated according to Bernstein's system by the symbols O, A and B, and corresponding respectively to the absence of any agglutinogen and to the presence of the agglutinogen A or of the agglutinogen B. Since each individual always carries two genes for the same character—one of paternal origin and one of maternal origin—he necessarily carries in one of his twenty-four chromosome pairs *two genes* determining his blood group. The two genes may be *AA, AB, AO, BB, BO,* or *OO*. Individuals with genes *AA, BB,* and *OO* are homozygous while those with genes *AB, AO,* and *BO* are heterozygous.

Gene A dominates gene O. Individuals with AO

are therefore similar to individuals with AA; like them, they have the agglutinogen A (group A). Since gene *B* also dominates gene *O*, individuals with BO are similar to individuals with BB; like them, they have the agglutinogen B (group B). Agglutinogens A and B are both present in individuals with AB, for there is no dominance of *A* over *B*, nor of *B* over *A* (group AB). Finally, there is no agglutinogen in individuals with OO (group O).

In France the distribution by blood groups is as follows: group O, forty-three per cent; group A, forty-two per cent; group B, eleven per cent; and group AB, three per cent. These proportions differ appreciably for different races.[2]

The inheritance of the blood groups is now clearly understood. An individual with type A, if homozygous (that is, with two genes for A), produces only gametes carrying gene *A;* if heterozygous (that is, with the combination AO), he produces in equal numbers gametes A and gametes O. Similarly, an individual with type B, depending on whether he is homozygous or heterozygous, produces only gametes B or half B and half O. An individual with type AB (necessarily heterozygous) always produces in equal numbers gametes A and B. An individual with type O (necessarily homozygous) produces only gametes O.

From what has been said it is easy to predict the blood groups of children born of different unions. For example, parents both of type O can produce only children of type O; parents of type A can produce children of either A or O; parents of type B, children of B or O; parents of AB, children of A, B, or AB, but never of O.

This brings us directly to the question of the determination of paternity, or rather of the *exclusion of paternity,* for blood analysis—let us hasten to add —*never* allows us to state that a particular individual is the father of a child, but it *sometimes* allows us to state that he cannot be the child's father.[3]

Take a child with type A, born of a mother from group O or group B; the father must carry the gene *A* since this gene could not have been supplied by the mother, and consequently he must belong to neither group O nor group B.[4]

Likewise, if the child born of a mother with type O belongs to group B, his father must carry the gene *B;* consequently he can be neither O nor A.

Or take a child O, born of a mother O. The father can be A (heterozygous), or B (heterozygous); he cannot be AB. In the latter instance, moreover, information concerning the blood group of the mother is not needed; a child O cannot have a father from the group AB.

The exclusion of paternity is obviously possible only in genetically favorable cases. Suppose that a child with type A or B is born of a mother from group AB. The father may be A, B, AB, or O; there is nothing to identify his blood group.

J. Carles cites a dramatic case in which an analysis of blood types made possible the identification of two children who had been interchanged. One child was abnormal, an imbecile; the father, Mr. X, suspected that the child was not his, and that at an early age his own had been exchanged with another one in the same maternity ward. An investigation revealed the possibility of such an exchange and led to the discovery of the normal child whom Mr. X claimed as his own. But "the parents of the normal child were no

less certain of their claim. The child whom they had
raised and pampered for six years, whom they had
nursed through his illnesses, this child they would not
give up in exchange for a sickly, helpless idiot; they
refused to listen to anything else, for the child belonged to them." Mr. X insisted on having analyses
made; it was determined that he belonged to group
A, his wife to group B, and the idiotic child to group
O. It was therefore genetically possible that the child
was his (assuming that Mr. X was AO and his wife
BO); but the normal child, because it belonged to
group AB, could not have been born to the couple
that had raised it, for the presumed father belonged
to group B and the presumed mother to group O. In
spite of vehement protestations on the part of the
presumed parents, the court ordered the exchange
of the two children.

This case shows what serious psychological effects
can result when biological principles interfere with
the private lives of human beings.

The results of blood tests have been used as legal
evidence since 1924. In France, the issue has never
ceased to meet with resistance. In 1935 the Seine
Tribunal declared the admission of such evidence
"contrary to the French law which holds that paternity, and consequently non-paternity, are not sus-
ceptible of direct proof."

The Nice Tribunal, however, admitted without
reservations the results of blood analysis (November
17, 1937); the same holds for the Marseille Tribunal
(1938) and for the Lille Tribunal (1947). The Aix
Tribunal requires the consent of interested parties
(1939), courts in Montpellier (1948) and in Pau
(1949) authorize the use of blood analysis in the de-

termination of paternity. Finally, on July 25, 1949, the court of appeals for the first time issued a decree recognizing in principle the right for the defense in a paternity suit to introduce as evidence the results of blood analyses.

Naturally, this course must not be followed too far. With ample feminine logic Andrée Tétry asks whether it is desirable for husbands to be able to require a blood test to be assured of their paternity when each child is born. Jealous husbands would make a mockery of justice. And we might for no good reason risk "discovering more bastards than people thought existed."

R. Savatier, a professor of law at Poitiers, thinks that "it is better to risk foisting on a couple a rare intruder than systematically to demolish the very walls of the conjugal edifice." Hirszfeld, in turn, states that he has refused several times to perform an analysis: "The serologist ought not to abuse the weapons at his disposal. . . . He must defend the sanctity of the family rather than encourage adultery."

Another genetic distinction related directly to blood groups has recently been established: the distinction between *secretors* and *non-secretors*.

Ordinarily the agglutinogens A or B can be detected not only in the individual's blood but also in his saliva, gastric juices, etc. In certain individuals, however, the agglutinogen does not pass into these secretions; according to Shiff, passage or non-passage is determined by a special gene which can exist in two forms: the gene for secretion (S) dominates the gene for non-secretion (s).

Among white Americans (in New York) 17.6 per cent are non-secretors.

Chapter VII

OTHER HEREDITARY CHARACTERS IN THE BLOOD; RHESUS SYSTEM

The presence of characteristic agglutinogens (M and N) has also been detected in human blood cells. Since the serum never contains a corresponding agglutinin, however, blood differentiation of this type imposes no precautions with respect to transfusions. Here it was possible to identify the agglutinogens only by injecting human blood into rabbits. Depending on the type of blood received, the animals will produce different antibodies (agglutinins): anti-M, or anti-N, or anti-M and anti-N.

The production of agglutinogens M and N is determined by a pair of genes M or N. Every human individual carries either two genes for M or two genes for N, or one gene for M and one gene for N. As in the case of genes A and B, there is no dominance of M over N, nor of N over M.

It is possible therefore to identify on the basis of blood factors three different types of individuals: MM (homozygous), NN (homozygous), and MN (heterozygous).

Another type of hereditary differentiation affecting the blood was discovered around 1939 by Landsteiner and Wiener. Here we can merely outline the basic facts pertaining to the *Rhesus system*.

If the blood of a rhesus monkey (*Macacus Rhesus*) is injected into a rabbit, anti-rhesus agglutinins will be produced in the rabbit's serum. These agglutinins are also capable of agglutinating blood cells in certain human beings, who are said for this reason to be carriers of the rhesus factor, or to be *Rh-positive;* other human beings, whose cells are not agglutinated by the special serum containing the anti-rhesus factor, are said to be *Rh-negative.* In Europe about 85 per cent of the population is Rh-positive.

Information about differences in blood types makes possible the avoidance of certain accidents involving transfusions. If Rh-positive blood is transfused into an Rh-negative individual, the latter will produce anti-rhesus agglutinins, with the result that a second transfusion of Rh-positive blood may bring about serious difficulties.

But what is most important is that the incompatibility of parental Rh factors may have dire consequences for the offspring.

The type of the Rh factor, whether positive or negative, is determined by a gene; an Rh-positive individual can be homozygous (two Rh-positive genes) or heterozygous (one Rh-positive gene and one Rh-negative gene); in the first instance, union with an Rh-negative individual will produce only Rh-positive offspring; in the second instance, half of the offspring will be Rh-positive and half Rh-negative.

When an Rh-negative woman carries an Rh-positive fetus as a result of her union with an Rh-positive man, anti-Rh agglutinins will be formed in her serum; they will not have time to act on the fetus responsible for their formation, but during a subsequent pregnancy an Rh-positive fetus may be seriously damaged by the maternal blood (hemolytic disease of the newborn).

What has just been said holds true in from 92 to 95 per cent of all cases, but the facts are actually much more complex. There are actually several Rh subgroups. Wiener posits the existence of a single gene capable of assuming *eight* different forms, while Fischer posits *three* different genes, each capable of assuming two different forms (C, D, E: *c, d, e*) and, because they lie so close to each other on the same chromosome, incapable of *crossing over*.[1]

It is important for the layman to know that some marriages are dangerous on account of the incompatibility of Rh factors, and to understand that the same man and the same woman who, together, produce defective children might have normal children with a different mate.

A. Tétry records the striking example of an Rh-negative woman who had given birth to several still-born children. She and her husband decided to have recourse to artificial insemination; after receiving sperm from an Rh-negative donor, she passed through a normal pregnancy and gave birth to a perfectly healthy child.

The proportion of dangerous marriages approximates 10 per cent; fortunately difficulties caused by the Rh factor are less frequent in reality than in theory, and this for several reasons, all of which have not been elucidated. The Rh-positive father can of course be heterozygous and therefore produce Rh-negative children; in addition to this, it may happen that the noxious agglutinins are not allowed to pass through the maternal placenta. Sometimes the mother proves incapable of forming these substances or forms them only after the third or even the fourth pregnancy. We should also note that a simple transfusion of Rh-positive blood can cause an Rh-negative woman to form agglutinins during her first pregnancy and thus eliminate any chance of her having even one healthy baby. Bessis cites the case of a young woman of twenty-three whose first child was stillborn because she at the age of eight (fifteen years earlier) had received a transfusion from her mother, who was Rh-positive.

Caution must therefore be exercised to guard against performing transfusions involving incompatible Rh factors.

Suggestions aimed at reducing the number of dangerous marriages include recording the Rh type on premarital documents, but severe preventive measures of this type are not mandatory. Infantile mortality resulting from the incompatibility of Rh factors is constantly decreasing as a result of therapeutic advances (from 70-90 per cent it has already fallen to 10-15 per cent). As soon as a diagnosis has been made, a premature delivery should be attempted whenever possible (after eight or eight and a half months), for it is during the last weeks of pregnancy that the agglutinins attack the blood cells in the fetus.

If worst comes to worst and deep jaundice occurs, it is necessary to resort to an exchange transfusion; in this process, the child's blood is drawn out and replaced by an equal volume of the appropriate type of blood from a donor. Naturally the father's blood must not be used. The process is not dangerous when performed by an experienced technician.[2]

The discovery of the Rh factor has of course been

put to use in legal medicine. The new blood test, complementing those used in determining blood groups, can help to prove that a certain individual is not the father of a child. For example, if the mother is Rh-negative and the child Rh-positive, the father must be Rh-positive.

Formerly it was assumed that a man unjustly accused of fathering a child had about thirty-five chances out of a hundred of proving his innocence; since the discovery of the Rh factor, he has at least a fifty-fifty chance.[3] In 1946 an American court based a verdict of non-paternity on the Rh factor; in this instance expert testimony was given by the celebrated specialist Wiener.

Chapter VIII

THE DETERMINATION OF SEX

We have so far neglected to discuss one of the most important hereditary characters, namely the sex of the individual.[1]

Today, it is known that sex is irrevocably determined in the fertilized ovum, that is, at the time of conception. The early determination of sex is clearly established by a comparison of identical and fraternal twins. The latter, produced from separate ova, are just as frequently of the opposite sex as of the same sex. But identical twins, produced from the same ovum, are always of the same sex.

Everything having to do with the determination of sex involves chromosomes, and more precisely, one of the twenty-four pairs of chromosomes which, we recall, are found in all the cells of the father and the mother. The members of the particular pair that has this important role are designated as *sex chromosomes*.[2]

In the ovum destined to produce a female—and, consequently, in all the cells of the female organism —the sex chromosome pair is composed of two like elements called *X chromosomes*. In the ovum destined to produce a male—and, consequently, in all the cells of the male organism—the sex chromosome pair is composed of two unlike elements. One of these corresponds to the X chromosome of the female, while the other, called the Y *chromosome*, is appreciably smaller.

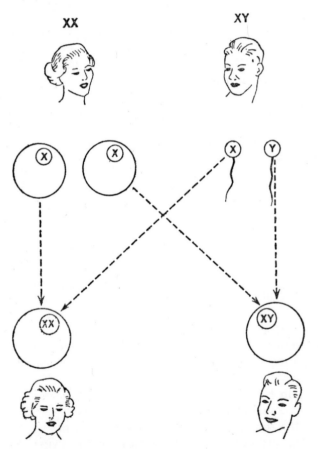

Fig. 6.—The determination of sex in man

According to certain writers, the X chromosome measures approximately four or five microns, and the Y chromosome measures one and one-half microns.

What is the origin of chromosomal differentiation in the fertilized ovum? Why is it that the ovum sometimes has the formula XX and sometimes the formula XY?

We have seen that at maturation the gametes receive only *half* of the chromosomes contained in the zygote or in the somatic cells—one member from each pair of chromosomes. In the case of the sex chromosomes the chromatic reduction will necessarily have different effects, depending on whether the female parent or the male parent is involved. In the female, who carries two chromosomes, all the gametes will receive an X chromosome; in the male, who carries an X chromosome and a Y chromosome, half of the gametes will receive an X chromosome and the other half a Y chromosome.

There are then two possibilities with respect to fertilization. Either the ovum is fertilized by a spermatozoon containing an X chromosome and, since it then contains two X chromosomes, produces a girl; or it is fertilized by a spermatozoon containing a Y chromosome and, since it then contains an X and a Y, produces a boy.

In short, the semen contains two kinds of gametes; one kind produces boys, the other girls. Since both are formed in equal numbers, and since fertilization occurs at random (that is, there is no reason why a certain ovum should be penetrated by one spermatozoon rather than another), the sex of the child is determined by *chance*. The probability of producing a boy or a girl is commonly called *simple chance*.

In roulette, for example, it can be predicted that if the wheel is turned a great number of times, black will appear almost as frequently as red; similarly, it can be predicted that a large number of births will comprise approximately the same number of boys and girls.[3]

According to R. Turpin, D. Deroche, and Schutzenberger,[4] statistical analysis could not reveal in certain couples the existence of a predisposition to produce either a greater number of boys or a greater number of girls. Attention has been drawn, however, to exceptional cases of "families of boys" and "families of girls."

In a family studied by Harris [5] there has been an unusual predominance of male births, dating back to the end of the seventeenth century. In ten generations, including thirty-five children, he counted thirty-three boys and two girls, one of whom was intersexual. This family is not very fertile; in every one of the men examined, the spermatozoa were extremely small.

Another extraordinary case is cited by R. Lienhart and H. Vermelin. In the family of Mrs. B, of Nancy, no male offspring has appeared in three generations.

Mrs. B's grandparents had six girls, all of whom married and had only girls in their families: the oldest of the six had eight daughters; the second, two; the third, two; and the sixth (Mrs. B's mother), nine. This totals twenty-seven girls for the second generation. The third generation, the issue of Mrs. B and of her seven sisters, is again made up exclusively of girls: twelve by the second, nine by the third, five by the fourth, four by the fifth, three by the sixth, two by the seventh, two by the eighth, and two by the ninth (Mrs. B). This totals thirty-nine girls, bringing the overall total to *seventy-two* girls out of *seventy-two* pregnancies distributed over three generations.

Since the fifteen husbands were related neither to each other nor to their wives, the exclusive production of female offspring must be attributed to the women alone.

Families of boys and families of girls constitute a difficult problem for the biologist. With respect to the first, we might assume that in certain families the Y chromosome contains a hereditary factor that prevents the formation of spermatozoa with an X chromosome; but for families of girls, we are almost forced to conclude that the transmission of the tendency to produce females depends on the maternal cytoplasm.

We can posit a factor which prevents the ovum from being penetrated by a spermatozoon containing a Y chromosome, or one that makes uterine secretions deleterious for Y spermatozoa, or one that makes the maternal environment toxic for male fetuses. For example, we might suppose that in the case of women who give birth only to girls, certain female hormones noxious to the male fetus are more readily introduced into the placenta or that the serum contains an anti-Y agglutinin. But these are unsubstantiated hypotheses.

Is the formula for the determination of male sex XY or XO? It has been established that the determination of sex depends on a chromosomal mechanism of the type described above, but cytologists are not in complete agreement on the chromosomal formula for the determination of male sex.

Painter, Evans and Swezy, Shiwago and Andres, Minouchi and Ohta, Keller, and many others assign to the male sex the formula XY; some writers, however

—among them Winiwarter, Oguma, and Kihara—hold that the formula is XO. According to the second group, the human male carries but one sex chromosome, the X chromosome, and has no Y chromosome; he therefore has one chromosome less than the female (forty-seven instead of forty-eight) and produces either spermatozoa containing the X chromosome (resulting in the formation of female zygotes) or spermatozoa containing no sex chromosome (resulting in the formation of male zygotes).

G. Herberer, to whom we are indebted for an excellent explanation of this delicate question, thinks that Shiwago and Andres have proven conclusively the existence of the Y chromosome in man; but Robert Matthey, the eminent cytologist in Lausanne, refuses to believe that the last word has been said. Matthey favors the formula XY:

> Does man have forty-seven or forty-eight chromosomes? An examination of the literature leaves us with an impression of confusion and with the conviction that the objective evidence is insufficient. I may well be wrong, but I think that probability favors the number forty-eight and the formula XY.

Furthermore, it is quite possible that certain divergences between cytological results relate to racial differences: Winiwarter worked with the white race, Painter with the black race, Oguma with the yellow race.

Finally, the existence of sex-linked characters transmitted exclusively from father to son (see Chapter IX) constitutes a powerful argument in support of the existence of the Y chromosome.

SEX-LINKED FACTORS IN HEREDITY

The sex chromosomes X and Y play a decisive role in the determination of sex. In addition they contain genes capable of determining general characters, and these genes are not transmitted in the same way as genes carried on somatic chromosomes.

Up to this point there has been no consideration of hereditary characters from the viewpoint of their belonging to either the father or the mother; the situation is different, however, when we deal with characters whose genes are carried by the sex chromosomes.

The X chromosome does in fact contain a considerable number of genes not found on the Y chromosome while the latter, which is smaller, contains several genes not found on the X chromosome.

The female, provided with two X chromosomes, obviously carries *a double complement* of the corresponding genes. They are therefore found in all her gametes (ova) and transmitted to *all her offspring*. The father, on the other hand, has only one X chromosome and *only one complement;* the corresponding genes are therefore found in only *half* of his gametes (spermatozoa), and these are the ones that produce girls, since they contain an X chromosome. In short, genes corresponding to the X chromosome are transmitted by the father *only to his daughters*.

Genes carried on the Y chromosome [1] belong exclusively to the father, who has but one Y chromosome and but a single complement of the corresponding genes; he therefore transmits them to only *half* of his spermatozoa, and these are the ones that produce boys, since they contain a Y chromosome. In short, genes corresponding to the Y chromosome are transmitted *only by the father,* who transmits them only to his sons.

As for the genes found in the section common to both sex chromosomes, they may be transmitted by either parent to a son as well as to a daughter, but their transmission nevertheless presents certain peculiarities (see p. 55).

The inheritance of certain characters is linked to the sex chromosomes. One such character dependent in human beings on the X chromosomes is *Daltonism* or the inability to distinguish between green and red.

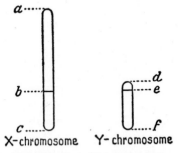

Fig. 7.—Sex Chromosomes

Drawing showing the regions to which sex-linked genes belong. Sections *bc* and *ef* are common to both chromosomes (homologous). Section *ab* is peculiar to the X chromosome; section *de* is peculiar to the Y chromosome.

The gene for Daltonism is dominated by the corresponding normal gene. Suppose that a woman with normal vision (carrying two normal genes in her X chromosomes) marries a man who is color blind. According to what has already been said, all their children will receive from the mother the gene for normal vision; the daughters will receive from the father the gene for Daltonism but they will be normal since the gene for normal vision is dominant. As for the boys, they will receive from the father no such gene —neither the gene for normal vision nor the gene for Daltonism—and will obviously be normal.

Children born of such a union are *all normal.*

The results are different in the case of a union between a Daltonian woman (carrying the gene for Daltonism in both of her X chromosomes) and a man with normal vision.

Here the mother transmits to all her children the gene for Daltonism. The father transmits only the gene for normal vision to his daughters. The gene for Daltonism appears in the boys, who are Daltonians like their mother (*crossed heredity*).

The results are also different in the case of a union between a normal man and a woman with normal vision who carries the gene for Daltonism.

Here the mother transmits the normal gene to one-half of her children (whether boys or girls) and the gene for Daltonism to the other half. But Daltonism appears in the second half only among the boys, who do not receive a normal gene from the father; it does not appear among the girls, who do receive this gene. One-fourth of the children will therefore be Daltonians (boys).

Finally, consider the union of a Daltonian man and

a woman who, though normal, carries the gene for Daltonism.

Here the mother also transmits to half of her children, regardless of their sex, the gene for Daltonism, and this trait appears not only in the boys, who receive from the father neither the gene for normal vision nor the gene for color blindness, but also in the daughters, who receive from the father a second gene for Daltonism. Half of the children are therefore Daltonians (boys and girls).

The union of a Daltonian woman and a Daltonian man will obviously produce only Daltonian children.

It is also obvious that a Daltonian female will issue only from the union of two Daltonians or from the union of a Daltonian man and a woman who carries the gene for Daltonism. Unions of this type are rare, and Daltonism is therefore much more frequent among men than among women (4 per cent of European men against 0.5 per cent of European women, according to Bateson).

Genes peculiar to the Y chromosome are less complicated. They are transmitted exclusively from father to son and are really *sex-limited* whereas the others are not, since they can manifest themselves in either sex, though not so frequently among women as among men.

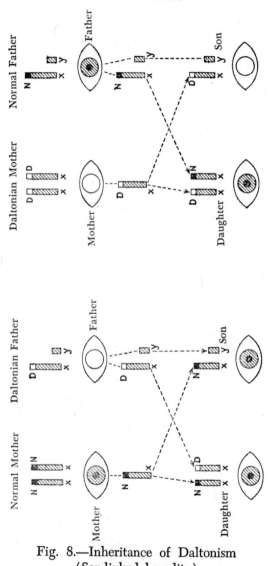

Fig. 8.—Inheritance of Daltonism
(Sex-linked heredity)

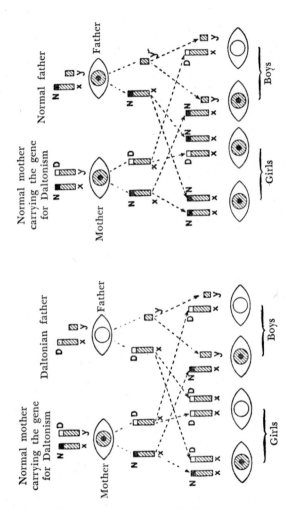

Fig 9.—Inheritance of Daltonism

Chapter X

LINKAGE

We saw in Chapter III that two chromosomes belonging to the same parental genome are transmitted independently of each other.

Suppose an individual carries two pairs of chromosomes, aa' and bb' (a and b having come from the father, a' and b' from the mother). It is obvious that four chromosomal combinations can occur in his gametes, namely ab, ab', $a'b$, and $a'b'$. The four combinations are equally probable or, to put it another way, the four categories of gametes must be equally numerous since there is no reason why gametes ab and $a'b'$—that is, gametes in which the chromosomes are paired exactly as they were in the two corresponding parental gametes—should be formed more frequently than gametes ab' and $a'b$—that is, gametes in which the chromosomes are paired in a different way.

This *total* independence of the chromosomes with respect to each other entails the *total* independence of their genes.

For example, if an individual received from one parent both the gene for the agglutinogen A and the gene for the agglutinogen M, and from the other the genes for agglutinogens O and N, there would be formed in equal numbers (since the genes in question belong to distinct chromosomes) *four* types of gametes, namely AM, AN, OM and ON. But the results are strikingly different with respect to the transmission of two genes that belong to the same chromosome.

Take an individual who receives from one parent both the gene for agglutinogen A and a gene for non-red hair (r), and from the other genes for the agglutinogen O and for red hair (R). Both genes belong *to the same chromosome;* there will be formed only *two types* of gametes, Ar and OR. The two genes will still be paired, *linked* in the gametes just as they were in the parents.

Linkage is actually not total, however, since *crossing over* will occur between members of the same chromosome pair, with the result that four types of gametes will be formed (*Ar, AR, Or, OR*) but *not in the same proportion.* Gametes carrying the combinations present in the parents (*Ar* and *OR*) will be considerably more numerous than gametes carrying new combinations (*AR, Or*).[1]

Linkage, though not *total,* is at least *partial.*

It would seem that from the painstaking study of certain human pedigrees conclusions could be drawn concerning the independence or linkage of particular genes and that it would be possible to determine whether or not two genes belong to the same chromosome.[2] Though such studies are easy and fruitful in dealing with animals which can be mated at will to provide requisite information, they are unrewarding in the case of human beings who, to add to the difficulty of our task, have a great number of chromosomes (twenty-four in each genome).

Still, it has now been established that the genes

for the blood group (A, O, B), the genes for the agglutinogen M or N, and the genes for taste deficiency are independent of each other and, consequently, that they belong to different chromosomes. Furthermore, it is believed that the gene for red hair is linked to the gene for the blood group, that the gene for asthma (certain types) is linked to the gene for congenital ichthyosis (certain types), that the gene for degree of hair pigmentation is linked to one of the genes that determine a reduction in the number of teeth. It goes without saying that all the genes on the X chromosome—and also all those on the Y chromosome—are linked together.

It has been possible to verify directly linkage of the gene for Daltonism and the gene for hemophilia, and even to determine that they are very close to each other on the X chromosome, for the frequency of their crossing over is not very high.

Of course it is only in the female, who carries two X chromosomes, that crossing over can occur in genes peculiar to the X chromosome. Crossing over can occur in neither sex in the case of genes peculiar to the Y chromosome. Finally, genes common to both the X and the Y chromosome can cross over in either sex: from one X chromosome to the other in the female and from the X chromosome to the Y chromosome in the male.

Transmission of X and Y genes, which are said to be *partially sex-linked,* poses problems too complex to be examined in an elementary work. We shall mention only the case of genes that determine dominant anomalies.

Suppose that a man carries such a gene in his

X chromosome (that is, he received one from his mother). He would transmit it to all his daughters but would not transmit it to any of his sons if there were no crossing over from X to Y; but as a consequence of crossing over, he may actually transmit it to some of his sons and may not transmit it to some of his daughters. He may therefore produce some abnormal daughters and some normal sons, but in each instance the number will be smaller than in the case of normal daughters and abnormal sons.

Or suppose that a man carries the abnormal gene in his Y chromosome (that is, he received one from his father). He would transmit it exclusively to his sons if there were no crossing over from Y to X; but as a consequence of crossing over, he may actually transmit it to some of his daughters and may not transmit it to some of his sons. He may therefore produce some normal sons and some abnormal daughters, but in each instance the number will be smaller than in the case of abnormal sons and normal daughters.

We can sum up the preceding facts by saying that in the case of X and Y genes that determine dominant anomalies, the majority of the abnormal grandchildren will be of the same sex as the abnormal paternal grandparent.[3]

To take a concrete example, there is a type of pigmentary retinitis which is hereditarily dominant. The study of pertinent pedigrees shows that when the sex of the progeny is the same as that of the defective paternal grandparent, abnormal offspring outnumber normal offspring (eighty-one to sixty), and that when the reverse is true, normal offspring outnumber abnormal offspring (eighty-three to sixty-four). This points to the conclusion that the gene is on the chromosomal section common to X and Y.

By determining how frequently a certain number of partially sex-linked genes cross over, J. B. S. Haldane was able to draw up a map of the region common to both sex chromosomes.

Chapter XI

THE INHERITANCE
OF COMPLEX CHARACTERS

Up to this point we have studied only the characteristics which are transmitted simply and according to the classical rules of Mendelian heredity. These are the characteristics which depend on a single hereditary unit—a single chromosomal particle—or gene. But many depend on the combined action *of several genes.*

It is easy to see that the process of transmission will be more complex in the case of characteristics that depend on the combined action of several genes, especially if they belong to different chromosomes. In order to understand the hereditary nature of such characters, we must have recourse to indirect methods, especially to the study of twins.

We have already spoken in several contexts of two individuals developed from the same fertilized egg and endowed with the same characteristics. They are called identical twins in contrast to fraternal twins, who owe their origin to two different eggs and carry dissimilar hereditary endowments.

If certain characters when they appear in one identical twin always reappear in the other—or at least much more often than they appear together

in fraternal twins—it is possible to conclude with a
high degree of accuracy that they are a part of the
individual's genetic make-up.

To reveal the hereditary nature of characters that
depend on several genes, we may once again turn
to the statistical method. When certain characters tend
to appear preferentially in certain progenes or families, it is safe to assume that they depend on genetic
forces.

Thus it has been possible to demonstrate, for
instance, the transmission of the predisposition to
longevity. There are some families whose members
live a long time and others whose members live not
nearly so long.

According to the American biologist Raymond
Pearl, the total obtained by adding the ages at death
of both parents and grandparents (*total immediate
ancestry longevity*, or T.I.A.L.) is quite high in the
case of long-lived individuals.

Pearl cites the striking example of a hundred-year-
old man—still living at the time the study was pub-
lished—whose parents had lived to be 97 and 101, and
whose grandparents had died at the ages of 104, 98,
106, and 93.

In another family embracing three generations, the
grandparents had an average life span of 91, the
parents 92, and the children 84; one of the grandparents died at the age of 102, one of the parents
at 97, and one of the children at 98.[1]

Long-lived individuals can be born to short-lived
parents, but as a rule when the lives of their ancestors
have been short, children are not likely to live far
beyond the age of 50. According to statistics compiled by Bell, if the father dies before the age of

60, the *average life span* of the children is 36; if both parents reach the age of 80, it is 52.

All that can be inherited from parents is of course the predisposition to be long-lived or short-lived; the actual life span depends largely on external circumstances (illnesses, accidents, stresses, etc.).

Among the characters that depend on multiple genes [2] are size (the genes for smallness apparently dominate the genes for bigness) and the shape of the skull.

Racial pigmentation offers an interesting peculiarity. The dark color of the Negro's skin certainly depends on *several genes,* probably *three,* which act together to produce a *cumulative effect.* The genes for blackness do not dominate the genes for whiteness; when both are involved in the production of the offspring (mulatto), the result is an intermediate coloration (light-brown).

If racial pigmentation were determined by a single gene, the union of two mulattoes would produce one pure white child and one pure black child for every two mulatto children.[3] But such is not the case, for we know that mulattoes generally have children with intermediate coloration. The reason is that the mulatto produces gametes that differ greatly with respect to the genes for pigmentation. Suppose that these genes are three in number; *abc* are the genes for blackness and *ABC* the genes for whiteness. The genetic make-up of the mulatto is *aAbBcC;* he forms eight kinds of gametes (*abc, aBc, aBC, abC, Abc, ABc, AbC, ABC*), with the result that two mulattoes offer $8 \times 8 = 64$ combinations of genes. Of these 64 combinations, only the combination *aabbcc* will produce pure black skin and only the combination

AABBCC will produce pure white skin. Thus it is not theoretically impossible but merely improbable for two mulattoes to produce children with pure white or pure black skin.

A mulatto and a white will as a rule produce only children lighter than the mulatto.

Intelligence and certain specialized aptitudes (musical, mathematical, artistic) seem to depend on multiple genes, but caution must be exercised in dealing with the inheritance of such aptitudes, for it is extremely difficult to distinguish germinal or hereditary forces from environmental or educational forces.

We can be sure that there are at the outset genetic differences relating to the scope and degree of specialization of intellectual capacities,[4] for this is attested by the existence of families of talented individuals (musicians, mathematicians, etc.) as well as by the striking similarity shown by identical twins with respect to their intelligence quotients.[5] Still, we cannot be very specific about anything relating to the transmission of gifts or aptitudes since intellectual evolution is strictly dependent on affective evolution, which can be shaped, advanced, or retarded by familial and social circumstances, by incidents that happen during early childhood, etc.

We must exercise even greater caution with respect to personality traits, tastes, and character. It seems that there are no hereditary predispositions toward jealousy, timidity, or avarice. The tendency toward *antisocial behavior,* however, seems to be partly hereditary. At least that is the conclusion drawn by Lange and others from their investigations of *criminality* among twins.

Out of 13 convicts with identical twins, 10 were

found to have a twin who had also been imprisoned
for a similar crime; against this, out of 17 convicts
with fraternal twins, only 2 were found to have a twin
who had also been prosecuted. Similarity of behavior
is clearly more prevalent in the case of identical twins
(genetic identity).

Other analogous investigations have shown that
out of 18 pairs of identical twins, 11 evidenced similar types of criminal behavior, while only 7 out of
19 pairs of fraternal twins evidenced such likenesses.

According to Grassberger, similarity in the behavior of identical twins is even more striking among
recidivists than among first offenders. This is not sur-
prising since a single offense can be the result of
chance circumstances and is less likely to reflect the
true character of the offender. In the case of multiple
recidivists, five-sixths of the identical twins displayed
similar patterns of behavior against only two-sixths of
the fraternal twins; and in the case of first offenders,
half of the identical twins and one-sixth of the fraternal twins.

Even assuming that these statistics are completely
valid, we must guard against concluding that there
actually are "born criminals," as Lombroso believed.[6]
All that they show is that human beings are not
equally capable of adapting to a given society, either
on account of their greedy or aggressive instincts or
on account of the weakness of their will or other ill-
defined character traits (exaggerated egotism, lack of
compassion, insensibility with respect to others). Nor
should we forget that the criterion for criminality is
somewhat relative; it is conceivable that in other
societies no worse than our own, there might be other

hereditary predispositions that would lead to anti-social behavior.

Finally, criminal predispositions probably vary in strength. Individuals who would under any circumstances become criminals are probably as rare as those who could not under any circumstances commit criminal acts.

Chapter XII

THE INHERITANCE OF DEFECTS

A great number of human anomalies and maladies are transmitted through heredity. Many of these defects are transmitted according to the ordinary Mendelian scheme—the abnormal gene either dominates the corresponding normal gene or is dominated by it. Both categories include genes linked to the sex chromosomes; these genes may belong exclusively to the X-chromosome or to the Y-chromosome, or they may be borne simultaneously on both chromosomes.[1]

Reference to Chapter IV will show that when the defect is dominant, the defective offspring always has a defective parent (continuous or direct inheritance), whereas when the defect is recessive, he almost always has two normal parents.

In the case of dominance, a defective individual (generally heterozygous) has one chance in two of transmitting his defect; two defective individuals (both heterozygous) will produce three defective offspring for each normal one; a homozygous defective individual will produce only defective offspring.

In the case of recessiveness, a defective individual is necessarily homozygous (since he would be normal if he carried the normal gene); with a normal individual he will produce only normal children; with a normal carrier of the same abnormal gene, he will produce half defective and half normal offspring; two normal individuals who carry the abnormal gene will produce three normal offspring for each one that is defective; two defective individuals will produce only defective offspring.

Thus in a family in which a dominant defect has appeared, a normal individual cannot transmit the defect; [2] against this, in a family in which a recessive defect has appeared, a normal individual can transmit the defect, for he can carry the latent gene.

Consanguine unions—marriages between first cousins, for example—are dangerous because they increase the probability of bringing to the surface recessive defects. It is logical to assume that two individuals with the same ancestry are more likely than two individuals selected at random to carry *the same bad gene*.

To clarify this important point, we shall consider the case of a rather rare defect, *albinism* (see p. 73).

Suppose that the gene for albinism is one hundred times rarer than the normal allele.

In any randomly selected individual each of the two chromosomes on which the gene is carried has one chance in one hundred of carrying the gene for albinism. There are accordingly two chances in one hundred, or one in fifty, that the gene will be found on one of his chromosomes. There is one chance in ten thousand ($1/100 \times 1/100$) that the gene will be found on both chromosomes; in other words, one individual in ten thousand will be *homozygous* for albinism.

Heterozygous carriers of the gene are therefore two hundred times (10,000/50) more numerous in this instance than defective homozygotes. This explains why most albinos are born of normal parents (heterozygotes).[3]

The probability that two heterozygotes (unrelated and randomly selected) will marry is 1/50 x 1/50 or 1/2,500. It is *much greater* if the two individuals are first cousins, for two cousins have one chance in eight of being common carriers of a particular gene.

Suppose that the father of one cousin (A) is the brother of the other cousin's (B's) mother. A has one chance in two of having received a certain gene from his father, and the father in turn had one chance in two of transmitting it to his offspring. The total probability is therefore ½ x ½ x ½, or ⅛.

A marriage between first cousins will therefore have one chance in four hundred (1/50 x 1/8) of producing albinos, whereas a marriage between unrelated individuals will have but one in 2,500.

If we assume that one per cent of all marriages are between first cousins,[4] we conclude that in 40,000 marriages there will be 400 of this type, and one that will produce albinos.

Of the remaining marriages (30,600), about 16 (that is, 39,600/2,500) will produce albinos. Thus out of 17 marriages that will produce albinos, one in 17, or about 6% rather than the 1% to be expected under normal circumstances, will be between first cousins.

The same principles apply to all recessive defects. It is easy to see that as the incidence of the defect in the population decreases, there is an increase in the ratio of consanguine marriages to the total number of marriages resulting in the production of defective offspring. Calculations would show, for example, that for a defect with a frequency of 1/1,000,000, the proportion of consanguine marriages would be 38 per cent.

According to the formula devised by Lenz and Dahlberg, if the incidence of marriages between first cousins in a given population is a, and if the incidence of the recessive gene is p^2 (the frequency of the gene being p), then the ratio of marriages between first cousins to marriages resulting in the production of defective offspring is

$$\frac{a}{a + 16\,p}$$

or, more precisely

$$\frac{a\,(1 + 15\,p)}{a\,(1 - p) + 16\,p}$$

Here are some figures, derived statistically, for different defects or recessive maladies.

Defect	Percentage of consanguine marriages
Pigmentary retinitis	15 to 17%
Familial amaurotic idiocy	14 to 15%
Alkaptonuria	30 to 40%
Hereditary deaf-mutism	9 to 23%
Mental defectiveness	3 to 18%
Phenylpyruvic idiocy	15%
Albinism	17%[5]
Congenital ichthyosis	24%

For a long time, even before genetics had made possible an exact interpretation of its effects, physicians had been noting the deleterious role of consanguinity.

In 1862 Boudin inveighed against the danger of consanguine unions, and in 1883 Alexander Graham Bell in turn called attention to the relation between such marriages and the incidence of deaf-mutism. It was also known that the number of defective children was higher in isolated regions (on oceanic islands), where marriages are usually between close relatives.

Darwin urged careful study of the consequences of consanguine unions. He pointed out that when the principles governing reproduction and heredity are better understood, ignorant lawmakers will no longer disdainfully reject plans for verifying by an easy method whether or not consanguine marriages are harmful to man.

But Darwin, like many naturalists of his era, thought that consanguinity itself was to blame. We have just seen, however, that it simply increases the probability that bad genes will be manifested. If all the genes were good, they could come indefinitely from the same source, and no harm would result. In animals, for instance, it has been possible to prolong consanguinity for tens of generations without impairing the offspring, so long as the genetic quality was maintained through rigorous selection.

Chapter XIII

EXAMPLES OF HEREDITARY MALADIES AND DEFECTS

Here we cannot attempt to enumerate all the maladies and defects that depend on a modification of man's genetic endowment. We shall simply mention some of the most characteristic.[1]

A well-known defect that has been studied extensively is *polydactylism*, a dominant defect characterized by wide diversity with respect to the degree of its manifestation or, in the language of genetics, its *expressivity*.

Among the individuals in the same progeny who have received the gene for polydactylism, some will exhibit the anomaly to the maximum degree (a well-developed sixth digit on each hand and on each foot); others will have the supernumerary digits only on their hands or on their feet, or only on one hand or on one foot; still others, instead of an extra digit, will have only a small nodule; and still others will have completely normal hands and feet but will nevertheless be capable of transmitting the anomaly to their children, who will exhibit it in varying degrees. The abnormal gene does not penetrate "on a visible plane" normal individuals who carry it; that is why it is said that the gene for polydactylism has reduced penetrance.[2]

Differences in the expression of the gene for poly-dactylism are probably due to the favorable or un-favorable action of other genes present in the heredi-tary endowment, but it is not impossible for environ-mental conditions, in turn, to exert some influence.[3]

Although rare, polydactylism has been known in the human species since antiquity. The Chaldeans believed that a six-fingered child was destined to con-quer the enemy. According to Megasthenius, an entire nation was composed of six-fingered men. Pliny notes that two daughters of Caius Horatius, as well as the poet Volcatius, had six fingers on each hand. The Bible speaks of a six-fingered giant, and Leonardo da Vinci in *The Last Supper* painted one of the apostles with six fingers.

The scientific study of polydactylism dates from the eighteenth century. In 1751 Godeheu, an admin-istrative official, had Réaumur present to the Academy of Science in Paris the pedigree of Gratio Kalleia, a six-digited Maltese who married a normal woman and had four sons, one of them six-digited. The latter in turn had four children, three of them six-digited.

At about the same time Maupertuis drew attention to the genealogy of Jacob Ruhe, a Berlin surgeon born with six fingers on each hand and six toes on each foot. Of his seven brothers and sisters, four were six-digited. The abnormality was inherited from his mother, Elizabeth Ruehn, who inherited it from her mother, Elizabeth Horstmann. He married a normal woman, Sophie-Louise de Thüngen, who bore him six children; of these, two boys had six digits.

Maupertuis, who attached great theoretical im-portance to sexdigitism (which he attributed to in-heritance and used to explain the problem of the origin of the foetus), tried to prove through mathematical reasoning that the anomaly was hereditary:

"An investigation which I conducted in a city of 10,000 inhabitants [Berlin] revealed that two men had this peculiarity. Suppose, even though it is improbable, that I missed three others and that on the average there is one six-digited individual in twenty thousand; the probability that the son or daughter of the six-digited individual will not be six-digited is 20,000 to 1. Further, the probability that the son and grandson will not be six-digited is 20,000 times 20,000 or 400 million to 1. Finally, the probability that the peculiarity will not continue through three consecutive generations is eight billion to 1. These numbers are so great that they are not approached by even the best documented phenomena in physics."

This remarkable passage shows that Maupertuis was one of the ancestors of mathematical genetics.

Numbered among the most celebrated six-digited individuals are Bulfinguer, one of the Duke of Würtemberg's ministers; Colburn, the mathematician; and Anne Boleyn, wife of Henry VIII.

Since time immemorial, writes Sigaud de La Fond, sexdigitism has occurred in several parishes in Bas-Anjou, "and this deformity has been perpetuated in spite of alliances with families not affected by the same physical defect." According to Ballowitz (1863), almost all the inhabitants of a little village in Isère had six fingers and six toes, and it is said that polydactylism was so constant in a certain Arab caste

(the Foldi tribe) that any man born with fewer than
six fingers was considered a bastard.

Another hereditary anomaly—also dominant but
uniform in its expressivity and having total penetrance
—is *brachydactylism* (shortness of the middle phalanges, which are sometimes fused with the terminal
phalanges). Though it is only a slight anomaly, it
makes it difficult for the individual to move his hands
and impossible for him to play the piano.

It seems that brachydactylism in the homozygous
state (two abnormal genes) is expressed through serious skeletal abnormalities:

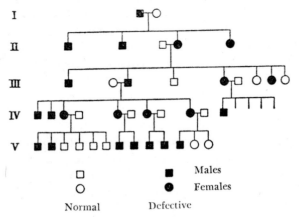

Fig. 10.—Pedigree of brachydactylism
(after Farabee)

In a progeny of brachydactyls, the marriage of two
first cousins, of whom one was certainly affected and
the other probably, resulted in the birth of a fingerless
and toeless child who died at the age of one.

It is probable that a number of abnormal genes are *lethal* or *sublethal* in the homozygous state.

Symphalangism (the fusion of two phalanges) is also a dominant character. One pedigree attesting this abnormality embraces fourteen generations, beginning with John Talbot (1390-1453), first Earl of Shrewsbury, a character in Shakespeare's *Henry VI;* moreover, when the distant ancestor's tomb was rediscovered, an examination of the skeleton revealed the digital abnormality.

There are a number of other abnormalities affecting the bones (*ectrodactylism* or absence of several digits, pincer-shaped hand, crooked little finger, shortness of the thumb, etc.). One of the most "spectacular" such abnormalities is *acheiropodia,* or total absence of hands and feet. It was identified by Peacock in a Brazilian family in which the father and three children were affected. A similar abnormality was found in a Hindu family in which 22 of 46 individuals (about half, that is) had but one finger on each hand. The abnormality is manifestly dominant. This example shows the magnitude of the effects that can result from the mutation of a single gene.

Hereditary fragility of the bones (dominant defect) is often accompanied by bluish coloration of the sclera and by hearing difficulties.[4]

Complete or almost complete absence of pigment (*albinism*) is a character that is clearly dominated by the normal character.

Albinos have white or extremely light blond hair; the iris is pink, for its transparence reveals the blood vessels at the back of the eye; in addition, they often have defective vision and other shortcomings (small

stature, reduced fecundity). This abnormality is quite
rare (on the average, one out of one hundred thousand), and occurs somewhat more frequently in
Austria. It even exists among Negroes: these "white
Negroes" were known during the eighteenth century;
they had excited Voltaire's curiosity and inspired
Maupertuis to write a famous *Dissertation*.

There are also piebald Negroes. In Louisiana a
piebald Negro woman gave birth to fifteen children
of whom seven were normal and eight piebald (dominant character).

Many skin disorders are transmitted by heredity.

Epidermolysis bullosa (tendency of the skin to
produce blisters) occurs in at least three forms, each
with its own mode of transmission: a benign form
(dominant); a more serious form accompanied by
torsion of the nails (dominant); a malignant form
accompanied by abnormalities relating to the teeth,
mucous membrane, the larynx, and eyes (recessive
and partially sex-linked).[5]

Xeroderma pigmentosum (recessive and partially
sex-linked) is manifested at an early age by excessive
sensitivity of the skin to sunlight. There appear red
spots and warty growths which may undergo malignant changes; afflicted individuals rarely reach adulthood. Their parents (heterozygous state) sometimes
have a tendency to be freckled; the character is therefore not completely recessive.

One striking case of *ichthyosis congenita* is famous
in medical literature. This is the case of the "porcupine man" (Edward Lambert), described in 1733 by
J. Machin. When exhibited in London at the age of
fourteen, he had a hard, scaly, insensitive skin covered

in certain spots (sides and stomach) by bristles. At birth his skin appeared to be normal; it began to turn yellow when he was about six weeks old; gradually it hardened and turned black. His parents were normal.[6]

According to Baker, who examined the "porcupine man" when he was forty years old, his skin was covered with great masses of dark brown warts; only his head, face, the palms of his hands, and the soles of his feet were exempt.

The "porcupine man" had six children, all afflicted with the same abnormality, which was perpetuated for two more generations. Since it appeared only in males, it would seem to depend on a holandric gene.

Baker stressed the contribution of the phenomenon to our understanding of the origin of the races of man:

> It seems that a whole race might have sprung from this individual . . . and if people had lost sight of its origin, it might have been mistaken for a distinct species.

Total absence of dentition (even the milk teeth) is transmitted as a sex-linked character in certain Hindu families; it is accompanied by a propensity for baldness, silky-textured hair, and the absence of sweat glands.

Other abnormalities transmitted as simple dominant characters: the absence of all the incisors, the absence of the upper lateral incisors, the absence or rudimentary condition of the canine teeth, brown-colored teeth (deficiency of enamel).

Deaf-mutism (when hereditary, for it is frequently due to an intrauterine infection) is transmitted as a recessive character. Still, the union of two genetic deaf-mutes may result in the birth of children with normal hearing, for several genes are capable of determining deaf-mutism, with the result that the effect of the normal gene contributed by one parent may compensate for the morbid gene contributed by the other.

The eyes afford many examples of Mendelian heredity. We have already mentioned Daltonism. This abnormality, which depends on a recessive sex-linked gene, occurs in 4 per cent of the population of European men; it is much rarer among women.[7] It was first described by the Scotch physician Dalton, a professor at the University of Edinburgh, who was apparently incapable of discerning the color of his academic robe.[8]

Total color blindness (*achromatopsy*) is an extremely rare abnormality transmitted as a partially sex-linked character.

Hemeralopia (inability to see in semi-darkness) is sometimes transmitted as a dominant character. This happened in the famous pedigree of Jean Nougaret, born in 1637; here the abnormality can be traced through ten generations, embracing 134 affected individuals. It is transmitted at times as a simple recessive, at times as a sex-linked recessive.

Retinitis pigmentosa (genetic types) is transmitted as a simple dominant character, as a simple recessive, as a partially sex-linked dominant, and as a sex-linked recessive (the latter mode being the most frequent). It entails progressive degeneration of the retina, pigmentary deposits, and vascular changes. It generally starts during childhood; the field of vision gradually narrows and blindness inevitably results.

Congenital cataract, the cause of many cases of blindness, is transmitted as a dominant character, as is *glaucoma.*

Along with visual defects go mental deficiencies involving blindness.

The terrible malady called *infantile amaurotic idiocy* is inherited as a recessive character. It usually manifests itself a few months after birth and always entails death before the end of the third year. It is marked by gradual diminution of visual acuity, muscular paralysis, and pronounced mental impairment.

Examination of the back of the eye reveals the presence of a cherry-red spot on the macula; the pyramidal cells of the cortex are deformed, as if distended by a deposit of lipoid substances.

Another type of amaurotic idiocy (*juvenile*) depends on another gene, also recessive; it differs clinically from the preceding by the absence of the red spot and by the appearance of the symptoms at a later time; it occurs at about the age of six and does not entail death until the period of adolescence.

Hemophilia, or failure of the blood to coagulate,[9] is a sex-linked recessive character.

The frequency of this defect in the male sex is about 1 in 10,000. No hemophilic women are known to exist, though in theory there ought to be 1 in 100,000 (1/10,000 x 1/10,000); whether this is due to lethality of the gene in the homozygous state or to the fact that it cannot be expressed in the presence of female hormones, is unknown.[10]

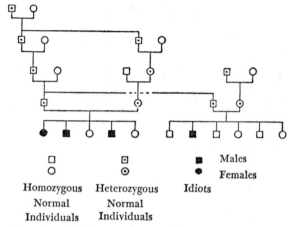

Fig. 11.—Pedigree of juvenile amaurotic idiocy
(after Sjögren)

Hemophilics rarely reach adulthood; women capable of transmitting the gene (heterozygous individuals or *carriers*) sometimes manifest slight irregularities with respect to coagulation (Andreassen).

A historic case of transmission of hemophilia is that of Queen Victoria of England, who transmitted the deleterious gene to the ruling house of Russia through the intermediary of the Hesse family and to the ruling house of Spain through the intermediary of the Battenbergs. Victoria received the gene from her mother, who had received it from her mother. Victoria's husband, Prince Albert of Saxe-Coburg-Gotha, belonged to a progeny of hemophilic carriers, though he himself was probably illegitimate.

Sickle-shaped red blood cells are dominant over normal cells. Some individuals with abnormal red

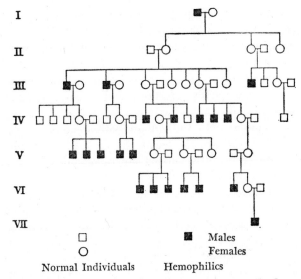

		Males
□		Females
○	Hemophilics	
Normal Individuals		

Fig. 12.—Pedigree of hemophilia (after Bulloch and Tildes)

blood cells have a severe type of jaundice (*congenital hemolytic jaundice*).

One of the most striking hereditary characters has to do with the white blood cells or leucocytes (*Pelger's nuclear anomaly*).

In normal individuals the nucleus of the leucocyte (especially that of the *neutrophil*, which predominates) at first simply assumes the shape of a sphere; later, after the cell has reached maturity, the nucleus divides into several lobes linked together by thin threads of chromatin.

In normal blood the proportions of different types of neutrophilic leucocytes are as follows: 4 per cent with uniform nuclei; 21 per cent with bilobate nuclei; 48 per cent with trilobate nuclei; 23 per cent with quadrilobate nuclei; and 4 per cent with nuclei divided into five or more lobes. The percentage of nuclei with no segmentation or with little segmentation increases with infections and inflammations; it diminishes, on the other hand, in the case of pernicious anemia. In individuals with Pelger's nuclear anomaly,[11] most of the leucocytes have single or bilobate nuclei; trilobate nuclei are rare, and segmentation never goes further.

This character is linked to a dominant gene. Contrary to what was at first thought, it has no relation to any tubercular or other morbid condition. Though not completely inoffensive (the leucocytes of afflicted individuals have a reduced capacity for defense), it can scarcely be said to entail grave dangers since it has been found among octogenarians.

By 1940, thirty-two families with Pelger's disease had been identified in different regions of the world (Germany, Czechoslovakia, France, Switzerland, the United States) and even among the Mongoloid races (Chinese, Japanese, Malay). None has yet been identified in England.

Among 16,316 subjects randomly selected from the population of Berlin, Nachtsheim found 16 with Pelger's disease, or about 0.1 per cent. The anomaly has also been studied in rabbits (Undritz, Nachtsheim), and, since the gene is not absolutely lethal, a few homozygous rabbits have even been produced. These "super-Pelger" subjects exhibit very grave anomalies: the nucleus of every leucocyte is uniformly rounded, with no trace of segmentation; in addition, the subjects are stunted and afflicted with osteal lesions. In the human species no "super-Pelger" has yet been identified.[12]

Among metabolic disturbances related to genetic constitution we cite first *alkaptonuria,* an anomaly marked by walnut-brown coloration of the urine. This coloration is due to the presence of a body (homogentisic acid) resulting from incomplete transformation of tyrosine and phenylalanine. Alkaptonurics probably lack a certain enzyme possessed by normal individuals. Sometimes they have dark-hued ligaments and cartilage, and they suffer from chronic arthritis. Alkaptonuria is almost always transmitted as a recessive character; nevertheless, one pedigree is known in which transmission follows the dominant pattern.

Another metabolic disorder is *tuberous xanthomatosis,* characterized by the development of nodules and tumors on the periosteum and tendons and due to an excessive quantity of cholesterol in the blood (there may be ten times the normal amount). This malady appears in individuals homozygous for the gene; in heterozygous individuals, the effect is lessened, and takes the form of simple hypercholesterolemia.

A peculiar type of mental deficiency, *phenylpyruvic idiocy* (described by the Norwegian biochemist Fölling) is related to a hereditary metabolic disorder characterized by daily excretion of a considerable amount—as much as one gram—of phenylpyruvic acid ($C_6H_5CH_2 \, CO \, COOH$). This acid produces a blue-green coloration, bright but fleeting, when a few drops of a 5 per cent solution of ferric chloride are added to the urine. In addition, the urine gives off an aromatic odor. Certain physical characters (reduced stature and cranial dimensions, kyphosis, widely spaced teeth, excessive pigmentation of the skin) and a tendency toward epileptiform seizures often accompany phenylpyruvic idiocy, which is in other respects compatible with near-normal health and a sociable temperament.

The anomaly—transmitted as a recessive character—is doubtless due to the absence of an enzyme that normally intervenes in the utilization of phenylalanine; mental deficiency probably stems from an insufficient rate of oxidation in the brain cells.

The frequency of the defect ranges, depending on the country, from 1/30,000 to 1/50,000. It seems to occur on a slightly larger scale in Norway.

A grave affliction, *Huntington's chorea*,[13] is accompanied by involuntary, irregular movements; it generally appears around the age of 35 and may not even manifest itself until after the age of 50 (12 per cent of the cases after 49); it is transmitted as a dominant character.

Other mental disorders (schizophrenia, epilepsy, manic-depressive psychosis, certain types of mental deficiencies) are more or less directly related to genetic constitution, but their mode of transmission has not yet been clearly elucidated. They probably depend on several genes; moreover, environmental conditions play an auxiliary role, though not a negligible one, in the development of symptoms.[14]

Genetic constitution influences resistance to infections. Certain families are more vulnerable than others to diphtheria, scarlet fever, and typhoid fever. Psoriasis occurs more frequently among brunettes than among blonds.

As for tuberculosis, studies by K. Diehl and V. Verschuer have clearly established that resistance varies. The same is true of cancer; while no definite conclusion can be drawn since its true nature is unknown, we know that heredity can create in the human organism conditions that favor in various degrees the onset of the affliction.

Heredity also plays a part in certain disorders through sensitization (asthma, eczema, hay fever, etc.).

Medical genetics, quite apart from its theoretical importance, has great practical worth in that by providing the physician with valuable data, it sometimes allows him to formulate a hypothesis or render a delicate diagnosis and subsequently to initiate proper therapy. It must not be thought that a disorder is necessarily incurable because it is hereditary. Diabetes, simply because it has a genetic origin, is no less responsive to insulin; the same applies to pernicious anemia and treatment with liver; hemophilia responds favorably to treatment with female hormones (estradiol or stilbestrol); vitamin E has a favorable effect on the evolution of Friedreich's disease.

It is even possible that in the future the appearance of certain genetic anomalies can be prevented. The experiments of Landauer, Sturkie, and Ancel have already shown that in animals certain physical conditions (lowering of temperature) or chemicals (colchicine) can counteract the expression of hereditary polydactylism.

Chapter XIV

MUTATION

Mutation—the transformation of one gene into another gene—is a general phenomenon in animate nature. The hereditary substance is generally stable; at rare intervals, however, a particle of this substance —a gene—undergoes a sudden modification affecting its structure and its properties, and no definite cause can be posited for the change. After the new allele makes its appearance, it becomes as stable as the original gene.

Mutations occur in the genetic endowment of Man as well as in that of every other species. For example, kinky or woolly hair may suddenly appear in the progeny of white Europeans who did not carry the character, or the blotched character may appear in a progeny of Negroes who previously were uniformly black.

Mutation can also produce genes for defects and disorders. Mutation is necessarily responsible for maintaining in the population a constant proportion of grave hereditary defects entailing certain or almost certain death before the age of reproduction; and in this instance it is even possible to calculate fairly accurately the frequency of mutations producing morbid genes.[1]

This calculation has been made for hemophilia, epiloia, amaurotic idiocy, achondroplasia, etc. For epiloia,[2] it is reckoned that in roughly one person in one hundred thousand, the malady is due to a mutation that has occurred in the genetic endowment of a parent. The frequency of mutation is higher for hemophilia as well as for achondroplasia.

Certain physical agents (X-rays, gamma rays given off by radium, ultraviolet rays) and certain chemicals (yperite or mustard gas, phenol, the sulfa drugs) can provoke mutations or at least appreciably increase their frequency. We should therefore take note of the potentially deleterious effects of certain therapeutic methods, notably prolonged irradiation on genes.[3]

While no precise data are yet available, physicians ought to be alerted to the danger, both to personnel involved in administering radiological treatments and to the patients themselves.[4]

Nor should we exclude the possibility of genetic mutation following treatment with certain medications (urethane, sulfa drugs, etc.).

Here is posed the controversial problem of the influence on offspring of chronic intoxications (alcohol, tobacco).

As for alcohol, a great number of experiments have been conducted on different animals (rabbits, guinea pigs, mice, rats, chickens); in these experiments intoxication was restricted to the father in order to exclude any direct influence on the embryo. The interpretation of the results is questionable. While Stockard (1923) finds characteristic lesions in the progeny of intoxicated fathers, most other researchers (particularly Durham and Woods) draw negative conclusions; and Elderton and Pearson go so far as to maintain that alcoholic intoxication of the parents causes the offspring to be more robust.

The question is raised in much the same way as regards chronic infections, notably syphilitic infections.

It was long thought that the effects of syphilis could be transmitted from generation to generation. People saw in the malady the mysterious hand of fate, capable of exerting an inexorable influence on the future of a progeny, and this opinion was upheld and popularized by such literary works as Brieux' *Les Avariés* and Ibsen's *Ghosts*. When a child was born with a malformation affecting the eyes, mouth, or skeleton, an accusing finger was immediately pointed at a hypothetical syphilitic parent or ancestor, and generally such a parent or ancestor was identified. The truth is that there was general acceptance of the implied notion that two normal individuals ought to produce normal children. We know today, however, that in human beings defective genes infest many, if not all, genetic endowments. The only question that can justifiably be raised is whether the syphilitic infection—either through the influence of the microbe itself or through the influence of the toxin—can increase the probability of mutation. And even this is extremely doubtful. Dr. Damy maintains that there is no basis for the assumption that syphilitic treponema are capable of provoking mutations.

Naturally, when the malady strikes the mother, it can be transmitted to the fetus through the intermediary of the placenta; a child so afflicted frequently dies before or shortly after birth. If he survives, he may fall victim to "hereditary syphilis" and exhibit diverse lesions; in reality, however, his affliction results from early contamination and not from any hereditary phenomenon.[5]

Nor should we regard as hereditary in the biological sense an abnormality or a malformation determined by certain intrauterine conditions. Women afflicted with measles during the first weeks of pregnancy frequently give birth to children with malformations (eyes, ears, heart). In the same way certain maternal deficiencies can result in lesions in the embryo. Here we are dealing with precociously *acquired* characters, not innate or inherited characters. As we shall see later (Chapter XVI), the distinction is fundamental, for acquired characters are themselves not transmissible to the individual's progeny.

MENDELIAN CHARACTERS

Hair, skin, teeth, eyes

Dominant	Recessive
Brown hair	Blond hair
Non-red hair	Red hair
Curly hair	Straight hair
Normal	Absence of hair
Absence of hair	Normal
Thick hair	Thin hair
Normal pigmentation	Albinism
White forelock	Uniform hair pigmentation
Striped skin	Uniformly brown skin
Red spots	No red spots
Scaly skin (ichthyosis)	Normal

Dominant	Recessive
Normal skin	Absence of hair on second phalangeal bone
Keratosis follicularis (sex-linked)	Normal
Epidermolysis bullosa	Normal
Normal	Epidermolysis bullosa (partially sex-linked)
Predisposition to sebaceous cysts	Normal
Anidrotic ectodermal sysplasia (absence of sweat glands)	Normal
Absence of all incisors	Normal
Absence of upper lateral incisors	Normal
Normal	Absence of upper incisors
Absence of permanent canines	Normal
Absence of second and third premolars	Normal
Rudimentary condition of canines	Normal
Normal	Absence of all teeth (sex-linked)
Brown teeth	Normal
Normal	Absence of median incisors (sex-linked)
Normal	Absence of the second lower premolar (sex-linked)
Translucent dentine	Normal

Dominant	Recessive
Gingival hyperplasia	Normal
Brown, hazel, or green eyes	Blue or grey eyes
Absence of iris	Iris without pigment (albinism)
Mongolian folds	No Mongolian fold
Drooping of eyelids	Normal
Microphthalmos (with idiocy)	Normal
Myopia	Normal
Normal	Myopia (simple inheritance or sex-linked)
Astigmatism	Normal
Megalocornea	Normal
Congenital cataract	Normal
Glaucoma	Normal
Hemeralopia	Normal
Normal	Hemeralopia
Retinitis pigmentosa	Normal
Normal	Retinitis pigmentosa (simple or sex-linked)
Normal	Atrophy of the optic nerve (sex-linked)
Normal	Daltonism (sex-linked)
Normal	Achromatopsy (partially-sex-linked)

Skeleton and muscles

Acrocephaly	Normal
Frontal hyperostosis	Normal

Dominant	Recessive
Mandibulofacial dysostosis	Normal
Craniofacial dysostosis	Normal
Cleidocranial dysostosis	Normal
Prognathism	Normal
Achondroplasia	Normal
Hereditary fragility of the bones	Normal
Absence of nasal bones	Normal
Funnel-shaped thorax	Normal
Multiple cartilaginous exostoses	Normal
Congenital dislocation of the hip	Normal
Brachydactylism	Normal
Lobster-hand	Normal
Symphalangism	Normal
Polydactylism	Normal
Ehlers-Danlos syndrome (laxity of the joints and hyper-elasticity of the skin)	Normal

Circulation and respiration

Dominant	Recessive
Hemolytic icterus	Normal
Predisposition to nosebleed	Normal
Predisposition to varicose veins	Normal
Hereditary edema of the legs	Normal

Dominant	Recessive
Agglutinogens A and B	Agglutinogen O
C, D, E (Rhesus system)	c, d, e
Pelger's anomaly	Normal
Multiple telangiectasia (Rendu-Osler's disease)	Normal
Normal	Hemophilia (sex-linked)
Resistance to tuberculosis	Sensitization

Digestive system, glands, metabolism

Dominant	Recessive
Normal	Hypertrophic pyloric stenosis
Hypertrophy of the colon	Normal
Polycystic kidney	Kidney
Diabetes insipidus	Normal
Diabetes mellitus	Normal
Normal	Alkaptonuria
Cystinuria (cystine not transformed into urea)	Normal

Nervous system

Dominant	Recessive
Taster	Non-taster
Congenital aphasia	Normal
Normal	Infantile amaurotic idiocy

Dominant	Recessive
Normal	Juvenile amaurotic idiocy
Huntington's chorea	Normal
Normal	Friedrich's ataxia
Atrophy of the auditory nerve	Normal
Normal	Glioma retinae
Otosclerosis	Normal
Epiloia (Bourneville's tuberous sclerosis)	Normal
Multiple neurofibromatosis (Recklinghausen's disease)	Normal

Characters linked to the Y chromosome

Webbed toes (certain types)
Hypertrichosis auricularum
Fusion of two or three teeth
Brauer's keratosis of palms and soles
Ichthyosis gravis

Chapter XV

THE DIVERSITY OF THE RACES OF MAN

We have studied the inheritance of a certain number of human characters. Our genetic inventory, though incomplete, points up one incontrovertible idea: the extraordinary diversity introduced into our species by the interplay of hereditary factors.

By taking into consideration agglutinogens O, A, and B, agglutinogens M and N, the factors in the Rhesus system, etc., we are now able to distinguish several thousand blood types; and serological genetics has by no means exhausted its possibilities.

Infinite diversity may result from the grouping of multiple characters capable of combining in every possible manner—different types of blood, pigmentation, pilosity, build, facial structures, etc., to say nothing of physiological differences, abnormalities, and morbid conditions.

One of the surest teachings of human genetics is the revelation of *individuality*, the personality of each representative of the species. Each individual carries a characteristic set of genes: through the mechanism governing the distribution of chromosomes, he receives at the time of conception a substantial endowment which identifies him and distinguishes him from everyone else. It can be said that, without exception,

each of us is a *unique* specimen. A particular assort-
ment of chromosomes is determined by chance at the
time of conception when two gametes come together;
this particular combination is but one of many possible combinations, and in all probability one that will
never again occur.

At the "inheritance lottery" the same number is
never drawn twice.[1]

The individualization of the human being, the
uniqueness proclaimed by the science of heredity, is
manifested in a striking manner in the case of grafts
between two individuals.

Contrary to what is usually believed, it is impossible successfully to graft an organ or piece of tissue
from one individual on another individual. The human
organism that receives the graft rejects it, with the
result that it soon dies and is reabsorbed. The only
type of graft capable of realization is that involving
two parts of *the same individual* (*autograft*), as
when a piece of skin is removed from the thigh and
transplanted to the forehead. And proof that it is indeed the uniqueness of the individual's tissue that
opposes the persistence of a graft involving a second
individual (*homograft*) is the fact that homografts
can be effected between two identical twins.

In the case of identical twins all organs and tis-
sues are interchangeable, so to speak. The method
can even be used to determine in doubtful cases
whether twins are identical; a small piece of skin
is transplanted; if the graft is successful, the twins
are identical, for among fraternal twins—who are
simply brothers—the graft is certain to be unsuccessful.

It is interesting in this context to consider the degree of individual diversity that may exist among the children in a single family. The differences between brothers or sisters is sometimes astounding; yet a little elementary mathematical reasoning will show that this is only natural.

Take a very simple case. Suppose that each parent carries only one pair of chromosomes (A and A', A'' and A''') and that A and A', A'' and A''' differ with respect to at least one gene. Each parent would form two types of gametes: gametes containing chromosome A or A', A'' or A'''. There would be four possible combinations of their chromosomes: AA'', AA''', A'A'', and A'A'''.

If each parent carried two pairs of chromosomes (AA', BB'; A''A''', B''B'''), there would be four types of gametes (AB, AB', A'B, A'B'; A''B'', A''B'', A'''B'', A'''B'''). Together the parents would produce sixteen types of chromosome combinations.

If each parent carried three pairs of chromosomes, there would be eight types of gametes and 64 types of chromosome combinations. The law is therefore as follows: For n pairs of chromosomes in each parent, there are 2^n types of gametes and $2^n \times 2^n$ or 2^{2n} types of chromosome combinations. In the human species, in which the chromosome pairs number 24, it follows that there are more than 16 million types of gametes and about 250 trillion types of chromosome combinations.

As a matter of fact, the number of possible combinations even exceeds this, for reduction division entails exchanges of genes between pairs of chromosomes (crossing-over).

The actual number of possible combinations is beyond the reach of the imagination.

What is the source of genetic diversity within the species? It must stem from mutation; in other words, the original genes must have become diversified during the evolution of the species and must have undergone molecular changes.

It is by no means certain, however, that *all* genetic differences arose within the species. In the case of certain genes at any rate, mutations were transmitted by our animal ancestors. For instance, the genes for the different blood groups already existed in anthropoid apes, as did the genes for gustatory sensitivity.

No problem is more difficult than *the problem of the races of man,* for we know no human group that can be considered as constituting a *pure race,* namely, one made up *exclusively* of individuals who possess certain genes that set them apart from individuals belonging to another group. It follows that the anthropologist with the help of the geneticist can only show that certain human groups differ relatively to the extent that they carry certain genes.[2]

William C. Boyd says that a human race can be defined as a population that differs significantly from other human populations with respect to the frequency of one or more genes. His definition is rather vague and necessarily quite arbitrary, for in each instance we must decide whether the difference in frequency is sufficiently pronounced and the differential genes sufficiently numerous to justify a racial distinction. But there is no other objective definition of human races and, on this point, Boyd is in agreement with all qualified geneticists, notably with Th. Dobzhansky, whose admirable investigations of the vinegar fly have contributed much toward clarification of the problem of racial differentiation.

An important body of evidence has already been gathered concerning the distribution of genes that determine blood groups. Tens of thousands of individuals, taken from all parts of the world, have been "tested" for blood type.

We have seen that in the French population, approximately 43 per cent of the individuals belong to group O, 42 per cent to A, 11 per cent to B, and 3 per cent to AB. The Basques—who in the opinion of anthropologists have a distinct origin—exhibit proportions that are appreciably different: 57 per cent belong to O, 41 per cent to A, 1 per cent to B, and none to AB. There is, then, almost total absence of the gene for B.

An examination of the distribution of blood groups in different parts of the world [3] reveals that the O group predominates among American Indians (91 per cent); in the Toba tribe, the frequency rises to 98.5 per cent, and in a certain Peruvian tribe, it reaches 100 per cent.

There are two regions in which the gene for B is especially prevalent: one part of central Asia, and one part of Africa, including the valley of the Nile.

In Europe the zones of least frequency for the gene for B are Scandinavia, the British Isles, and the Iberian peninsula. The gene for B seems to be lacking in Australia and lacking or almost lacking among the aborigines in North America; in South America, it seems to be equally rare.

Though a mistake in diagnosis cannot be ruled out, it would seem that certain Peruvian mummies presumed to date from the pre-Columbian age exhibit the gene for B.[4]

In Germany the *B* gene increases in frequency

from west to east and continues to increase in Poland and in Russia; against this, in the Iberian peninsula it decreases from east to west; in Italy, it increases from north to south.

Turning to the distribution of the A gene, we find that in contrast to the B gene, it is not absent from any major part of the world. Still, it is very rare among certain North American tribes even though widespread among others. It abounds in the northern and northeastern parts of Europe but diminishes in frequency as we move toward Southeastern Asia. It exceeds 60 per cent among the Lapps in Sweden but falls to 25 per cent among the Chinese and Manchurians, and to 18 per cent among the Indians.

It was first thought that the A gene, almost universally distributed, was older than the B gene, assumed to have arisen through mutation; but today it is generally acknowledged that since its beginning the human species has had both genes in its genetic endowment.

As for the M and N blood factors, they are of approximately the same frequency in Europe and in Asia; but N is relatively rare among the American aborigines and widespread among the aborigines of Australia.

The Rh-negative factor (found among 13-17 per cent of Europeans and white Americans) is not found in certain large areas of the world, namely among the American Indians, the Papuans, the Maoris, and the Siamese; it is very rare among the Chinese and the Japanese; it apparently is found among African Negroes. Among the Basques its incidence is quite high (30 per cent).

On the basis of all these data, certain authors

have suggested the genetic classification of the races
of man according to blood characters. The first attempts at serological classification were made by Ot-
tenbert, Lahovary, and Wiener; the most recent attempt is that of Boyd, who divides the human species
into *six* basic groups: (1) ancient Europeans (a hypothetical group represented today solely by the
Basques); (2) Europeans or Caucasoids; (3) Africans
or Negroids; (4) Asiatics or Mongoloids; (5) American Indians; and (6) Australoids.

Blood characters today have no more intrinsic
worth than other hereditary characters, but they are
better known than any of the others with respect to
genetic determinism; furthermore, they are eminently
stable, impervious to environmental effects, and remarkably constant in their distribution throughout a
given population.[5]

Physical stature, for example, is modified by external conditions (nurture, climate); moreover, not
much is known about the genes that determine stature.
The situation is the same for the shape of the head.
It was more than a century ago that the Swedish
anatomist Retzius drew the attention of anthropologists to the cephalic index (the ratio of the width of
the cranium to its length): a man is said to be
dolichocephalous when the ratio is smaller than .75,
brachycephalous when it is larger than .80, and
mesocephalous when it falls between the two limits.
The vogue once enjoyed by the cephalic index and
the use to which it was put by certain theoreticians
(Vacher de Lapouge, Gobineau) are matters of rec-
ord. It was even maintained that fundamental mental
qualities were linked to the cephalic index, and the
fate of civilization was said to hinge on dolichocepha-

lics. But the facts are by no means clear. There is no clearcut separation, as Weidenreich has shown, between the three categories; besides, it is quite likely that external conditions (hardness or softness of the crib, quality of alimentation) can influence the cephalic index. In any event, the genetic factors controlling the cephalic index are obscure.

It is specious to attempt to define a race through cranial measurements. The same holds for the nasal index and for hair type. And even in the case of pigmentation of the skin, we must not forget that the amount of cutaneous pigment varies considerably among individuals of the same race and cannot be determined with exactitude.

Among the genetic differences for which anthropology is beginning to collect data, we again find those relating gustatory sensitivity to phenylthiocarbamide. Among most Europeans, it has been found that about 75 per cent are tasters; the figure reaches 100 per cent among the American Indians, however, and falls to 50 per cent in Wales.

The incidence of baldness varies according to race. Among the English, 13 per cent of the men lose their hair prematurely, while bald men are never found among the Navaho Indians.

There are also racial differences relating to sensitivity to diseases and intoxications. Mediterraneans are very sensitive to the poison of *Vicia faba;* smallpox is benign for Mexicans but severe for Indians and North Americans; measles are benign for whites but dangerous for American Indians and Melanesians; Latins are less sensitive than Anglo-Saxons to scarlatina; nervous types of syphilis are much less common among whites than among Negroes or Chinese. Primitive cancer of the liver is widespread among the Chinese (28 per cent) and Javanese (55 per cent) but rare among Europeans (0.3-1.3 per cent).

The existence of intellectual differences among races has never been objectively demonstrated. According to Boyd, it is impossible to affirm that one race differs essentially from another with respect to important characters like intelligence or adaptability. This does not of course rule out the possibility that certain races have an advantage over others, by virtue of their genetic equipment, with respect to the faculties most highly prized by western civilization,[6] but even such an advantage would not imply the *absolute* superiority of one race over another.

Finally, it should be noted that racial differences —apart from the fact that they are quantitative rather than qualitative—probably depend on a relatively small number of genes by contrast with the impressive total (tens of thousands) that makes up the genetic endowment of the species.

All men, regardless of race, are identical with respect to the vast majority of their genes. The anthropologist Glass estimates, for instance, that Negroes and whites exhibit no more than six genetic differences. His estimate seems too moderate to Boyd, but even if there were as many as twenty or thirty, the difference between whites and Negroes would still be infinitesimal in view of the vast legacy common to both races, and would certainly be less than the difference than can exist between two whites.

Racial characteristics are therefore of no great significance from the viewpoint of either the species or the individual.

In short, we should neither exaggerate the im-

Chapter XVI

THE INHERITANCE
OF ACQUIRED CHARACTERS

We have stated repeatedly that an individual's characteristics are determined by the genetic endowment transmitted by his parents through the intermediary of the germ cells and by the environmental conditions that prevail during the course of his development. In this context, we have often called attention to the *plasticity* of the human organism and the manner in which a number of characters can be radically modified by external factors, such as light, temperature, and alimentation. Furthermore, we have observed that moral and social factors are of considerable importance in the development of the intellect.

But is the influence of the environment on the human personality purely individual—that is, strictly limited to the individual on which it is exerted—or can it make itself felt to some degree in offspring through the interposition of a modification carried in the germ cells?

In other words, when an individual is modified by his environment, is his genetic endowment also modified, and in the same direction?

Here we come to the crucial question, so often

debated in biology, of the transmissibility of characters that are acquired by the individual or, more succinctly, of the *inheritance of acquired characters*.

To clarify matters and avoid any misunderstanding, we introduce concrete examples:

A European has been living in a tropical environment with the result that his skin is more heavily pigmented than it would have been if he had remained in his homeland. Will his children inherit more heavily pigmented skin or at least skin better adapted to pigmentation?

A second individual through methodical training has developed certain muscles. Will his children inherit muscular fascicles somewhat better developed or somewhat better adapted to profit from exercise?

A third individual through diligent study has exercised his cerebral faculties. Will his children inherit a more vigorous brain or a brain better suited to intellectual pursuits?

The biologist will answer all three questions—which are really one and the same—in the negative. The children produced by the three men will be exactly the same as if the first had not been living in a tropical environment, the second had not practiced gymnastics, and the third had not devoted himself to the cultivation of his mind.

Such an answer often takes the layman by surprise. The biologist's categorical statement requires a few words of explanation. Biology provides us with one powerful theoretical argument. We simply cannot conceive of any way whereby a modification of the skin, muscles, or brain could be *inscribed* or registered in the germ cell, which contains neither skin, nor muscle, nor brain, nor even a rudiment of any of them.

To be sure, it might be assumed that through the subtle influence of organic solidarity, a modification of the skin, for example, might entail a general modification of the body, including the blood, and that in this way the germ cells might be slightly modified. But this does not explain how or why the modification would result in the identical reproduction of the parental modification in the succeeding generation.

In short, while it may not seem impossible for a slight physical change to make its influence felt throughout the organism and even on the germ cell, it does seem impossible for the germ cell to "photograph," as Darwin once expressed it, the physical modification.

Apart from this theoretical argument, biology can invoke a number of experiments to disprove the transmission of acquired characters. These experiments, conducted with a view to demonstrating such a mode of inheritance, yielded only *completely negative results*. They were conducted on mice, rats, rabbits, butterflies, vinegar flies, etc.; and they were designed to provide data concerning the effects of alimentation, temperature, light, the acquisition of conditioned reflexes, etc.[1]

In recent years there have been many rumors concerning the experiments of Soviet biologists who subscribe to Michurinism and who maintain that they have demonstrated the transmissibility of acquired characters. But, in the first place, their hypothesis has been demonstrated in no other laboratory; it follows that we are justified in assuming that an element of error entered into the demonstration, as has so often happened in the past.[2] Furthermore, it must be noted that announcements of the results achieved by the Michurinists have borne the mark of ideological fervor, and this of necessity makes them suspect in the eyes of those who search for truth.

Certain biologists, while they agree that the transmission of acquired characters cannot be observed within the limitations of our experience, refuse to deny the phenomenon and maintain that it is indispensable in explaining the genesis of species. Our experiments are unsuccessful, they say, only because their duration is too short; to be decisive, they would have to last for centuries, if not for millennia. A reply to their objection is obviously impossible; but what matters, from the human viewpoint, is to know that on the practical plane, the life history of the parents apparently has no effect on the genetic constitution of the child.

It has at times been alleged that the existence of families of mathematicians or musicians supports the thesis that acquired characters are transmissible. But aside from the role that education and imitation may have played in the acquisition of familial talents, the fact that the child possesses the same gifts as the parent simply indicates that he has inherited the genes that determine these gifts. Under such conditions the parent transmits to the child all or a part of his aptitudes; he transmits to the child no part of that which the cultivation of his intellect or the development of his art has contributed to his aptitude.

Whether a talented individual cultivates his natural gifts or lets them lie fallow has no bearing on the genetic quality of his progenitor: if Bach's father had never played the organ, the genius of his son would not have been diminished.[3]

We need to clear up one further misunderstanding concerning the transmission of a state of immunity or a power of resistance with respect to certain diseases. We can be sure that *natural* immunity, which has a genetic origin, is transmitted; but this does not hold true for immunity which is *acquired*, either through vaccination or as a result of an infection.

Through the antibodies in her blood the mother can obviously transmit to the fetus a certain degree of acquired immunity, but here, aside from the fact that we are not dealing with heredity in the strict sense, the child will soon lose his immunity. As for the father, he cannot transmit an acquired immunity through his reproductive cells.

Let us note in passing, therefore, that there is no basis for the hope that immunities created artificially through medical methods will become part and parcel of the genetic endowment of the species. Acquired immunity, like all other acquired characters, must be reacquired by each generation.

Vaccination procedures, if in some way they affect the race, can exert only an unfavorable influence since—fortunately—they act counter to the inexorable force of natural selection by enabling weak individuals to resist infections.

Related to the inheritance of acquired characters is the false notion of inheritance through impregnation or *telegony*. Here a few words on the subject are in order.

It has sometimes been held that a woman's genetic potentialities could be modified under the influence of the fetus carried in her womb. It was thought, for example, that a woman who had mated with a Negro might subsequently, on mating with a white, produce children with Negroid features.

This prejudice, founded on pure fantasy, is held by many breeders, who obstinately believe that impregnation affects the heredity of domestic animals.

In biology, paternity is never anything other than direct paternity.

Chapter XVII

EUGENICS AND CONTROL OF HEREDITY

If the inheritance of acquired characters has no basis in fact and the effects of civilization are not imprinted on the genetic endowment of the human species, then we can expect no genetic improvement as the result of the material or moral amelioration of society.

One should even ask whether this amelioration has not, in the long run, exercised an unfortunate influence on the quality of the genetic endowment. Indeed, natural selection formerly exercised a rigid control over populations, eliminating many weak, deficient, or defective individuals. Today its influence is no longer felt, or is much less severe, as a result of progress in the field of medicine, surgery, hygiene, public welfare programs, and philanthropical undertakings which permit the survival of individuals who under primitive or less civilized conditions would have succumbed inevitably before reaching the age of reproduction.[1]

We should of course have no misgivings about this state of affairs. It is the duty and the privilege of our civilization to prolong the lives of those not equipped to live under natural conditions. But we owe it to ourselves to examine the genetic conse-

quences of the absence of selection, perhaps with a
view toward compensating for it through voluntary
control of human reproduction.[2]

Thus we come to the important problem of
eugenics.[3]

As a methodical study of measures appropriate
to safeguarding the genetic quality of future generations, eugenics is of relatively recent origin, yet it has
its roots in considerations dating back to the distant
past. Since ancient times man has been able to verify
—by observing either his own species or different
species of domesticated animals—the transmission of
certain individual characters, and his observations are
recorded in his legislation.

Hebraic law was opposed to the marriage of epileptics, lepers, tuberculars, and alcoholics; the Talmud
discourages marriage between individuals when both
are abnormally tall or short, when both are extremely
light-complexioned or dark-complexioned, or when
one of them comes from a family afflicted with certain
defects.

The laws of Manu forbid marriage into families
afflicted with tuberculosis, elephantiasis, or epilepsy.

Among the Greeks, the eugenic idea is expressed
not only in the Spartan custom of eliminating defective children but also in the writings of philosophers. Theogenes of Megara (548 B.C.) registered
astonishment:

> One would not buy livestock without exam-
> ining them carefully, nor a horse without
> knowing whether it comes from sturdy stock;
> yet a respectable man will receive as his wife a
> miserable woman born of a worthless father.

. . . Chance intermingles the races, and this odious mixture debases the human species. . . .

That was the protestation of a wise man against violation of biological selection in the pursuit of wealth.

A century later Plato himself set forth through Socrates a whole program of eugenic marriage. The aim of an ideal Republic is to make marriages "as sacred as possible," that is, as advantageous to the state as possible; and to achieve this, it behooves us to follow the example set by breeders of hunting dogs and of birds of prey:

> What do they do when they wish to breed their animals? They choose those that are superior. In the same way, if we do not want the human species to degenerate, we should unite the best of either sex as often, and the inferior with the inferior, as seldom as possible. The children of the "best" will be brought up by the state while those of the "worst" will be put away in some remote and mysterious place. . . . Moreover, to avoid protests on the part of the "worst," magistrates charged with regulating matings will have recourse to a fraud: they will pretend that mates are selected by lot so that the "worst" will attribute their misfortune solely to chance.

The eugenic viewpoint was to remain dormant for more than two thousand years only to reappear in the seventeenth century in Campanella's *City of the Sun* and in Thomas More's *Utopia*. More would have future mates submit to a medical examination; for his part, Campanella has in the government of his fictitious city a "department of love" created to oversee marriages and the procreation of children.

In the preamble to a Swedish law of 1757, it is stipulated that marriage between epileptics is forbidden because "the malady called idiopathic epilepsy is transmitted by parents to their children and their children's children."

In 1779, Johann Peter Frank, a German doctor, proposed eugenic measures in his *Complete System of Medical Policy*. And in 1803, in an amusing essay titled La Mégalanthropogénésie, the French publicist Robert Le Jeune advocated the marriage of eminent men and distinguished women with a view toward producing intelligent children:

> Whereas Europeans spare nothing to heighten the beauty of chargers, to improve wool-bearing animals, and to perpetuate the race of good bloodhounds, is it not shameful that man has been abandoned by man?

Darwin in his *Descent of Man* declared himself an advocate of voluntary eugenics: According to Darwin, marriage ought to be prohibited in the case of individuals whose physical or mental condition is markedly inferior; but to give expression to such hopes is utopian, for we cannot even begin experimentation until the laws of heredity are thoroughly understood.

Finally, around 1870 Francis Galton, Darwin's cousin, founded scientific eugenics. According to Galton, its object is two-fold: to impede the multiplication of the unfit, rather than to allow them to come into the world only to die prematurely (*negative eugenics*); and to improve the race by favoring the reproduction of the adept through early marriages and attention to their offspring (*positive eugenics*). In 1904 Galton introduced a course in eugenics into the curriculum of the University of London and gave the state a eugenics laboratory.[4]

Also worth noting, among the French advocates of eugenics, are Vacher de Lapouge, Molinari, Henry Cazalis (*alias* the poet Jean Lahor), who proposed the creation of a "prenuptial certificate," and finally, Charles Richet who, in an enthusiastic book [5] prophesied that human selection would be "the sole concern and supreme challenge of future generations."

In the light of modern genetics, which teaches us that certain defects are transmitted from parent to child with almost mathematical regularity, the eugenic ideal seems incontestably well founded. But through what measures can we reasonably expect to attain the desired result?

Sterilization is obviously the only really effective means of preventing a defective individual from procreating; and as a matter of fact, certain countries —the United States (27 states), Canada, Sweden, Denmark, Switzerland (Canton of Vaud)—have enacted legislative measures providing for eugenic sterilization.[6]

Sterilization can be effected in either sex by X-rays, by radium rays and, preferably, by surgery. The male undergoes a *vasectomy*, or section of the vas deferens.[7] It is a painless operation, performed in a few minutes under local anesthesia; cicatrization is accomplished in five or six days; sexual potency is not altered. Intervention is somewhat more serious in the case of the woman, for it is necessary to open the abdomen and ligate the uterine tubes or sever them at the uterus.[8] Mortality, though extremely low, is not unknown (0.41 per cent according to Bauer, 0.12 per cent according to Gosney); the result is not always definitive since the tubes have a certain power of regeneration.

Statistics compiled since 1943 indicate that to date 38,087 persons in America have submitted to legal sterilization; in Sweden, the number presently exceeds 15,000.

The legality of eugenic sterilization has evoked heated discussion. In extreme cases—for instance, the dominant hereditary anomaly called acheiropodia, consisting of total or partial absence of hands and feet— it seems incontestable that society has the right, if not the duty, to prevent procreation on the part of defective individuals. But such cases are admittedly rare, and the question arises as to whether their existence is sufficient to justify the adoption of measures strongly opposed in principle to our traditional concepts of individual freedom and dignity.

Through the application of eugenic sterilization, we could obviously weed out in little enough time many of the dominant defects against which we directed our campaign; but we would be unable to banish them completely, for through mutation, they are forever reappearing in the hereditary endowment of the species. Nor could we reach through sterilization the defects which, like Huntington's chorea, manifest themselves after the defective individual has achieved procreation.

Serious recessive defects, which outnumber dominant defects, could be attacked through sterilization.

Here progress would be slow, however, and success only partial since the defects are generally transmitted by normal individuals who are carriers of the recessive genes. To lessen appreciably the incidence of defects, it would be necessary to operate on many generations (68, according to some calculations, in order to reduce the frequency of a gene from 1/1000 to 1/10,000; 2,000 or 3,000 to eradicate it almost completely).

Not too much can be expected, then, from eugenic sterilization. Moreover, certain abuses are always to be feared when society is given such powers over the individual. It would seem that the greatest good will come from publicizing genetic principles and making future parents aware of their procreative responsibility.

It would be unwise to exaggerate the importance of the "prenuptial certificate" championed so long by Louise Hervieu, but its adoption is highly commendable, for it should contribute in the long run to the protection of the health of the species.

An individual who knows that he is a carrier of a deleterious gene—whether dominant or recessive—should be allowed to submit *voluntarily* to sterilization. L. Hogben, a dedicated eugenicist, thinks that the English law is at fault, for it prohibits parents who carry the gene for familial amaurotic idiocy [9] from avoiding the risk of propagating the dreadful malady by submitting to a simple, harmless operation.

In cases of this kind, sterilization should be permitted by law; in addition, it should be suggested and recommended by experts.

Consanguine unions offer some disadvantages from the genetic viewpoint.[10] Perhaps it is going too far to say, with Alexis Carrel, that marriage between first cousins is in principle a reprehensible act, but it is important to inform "the man in the street" in no uncertain terms of the danger which such unions entail—a danger to which he would probably hesitate to expose himself if he were properly informed.

As a general rule, the biologist or physician ought in all circumstances to provide candidates for a "dangerous marriage" with detailed information as to the nature and probability of the risk they will incur.

A deaf mute, for example, is almost certain to have normal children if his wife is normal, but his children will all carry the bad gene, with the result that he will have had a part in spreading it throughout the population. Naturally, he should avoid marrying a woman who, though normal, is a close relation.

Once the people have received appropriate instructions, it is their obligation to consider their responsibility to their progeny and to society. Their decision may be affected by a number of factors: by the gravity of the defect (from the viewpoint of health, esthetics, or the physical ineptitude that it might entail); by the material circumstances of the children to the extent that they are foreseeable; and especially by the character of the individuals themselves, who may be either irresponsible or conscientious—or to put it another way, by their *coefficient of eugenic sensitivity*.

There is still another form of eugenics, namely *positive* eugenics, whose aim is to encourage the multiplication of individuals who carry the best hereditary qualities. In this area diverse measures have been advocated. The most effective but also the most daring of these has been advanced by the American biologist H. J. Muller, who would practice artificial insemination on a great number of women, using superior men as donors. It is reasonable to assume that after several generations this would result in an appreciably higher level of intelligence among the population; but any attempt to institute such a program would encounter staggering social, moral, and sentimental difficulties.

Whatever opinion of eugenics one holds—and we have tried to show in these few pages both what its solid biological foundation is and what the limits of its application should be—we must guard against imputing to it any political ramifications.

"Eugenics," said Bertrand Russell, "will never mix with democracy." His judgment, though neatly expressed, seems rash. Eugenics has at times seemed suspect to staunch advocates of democracy, but this stems mainly from the fear that the victims of enforced eugenics would be drawn from the lower classes, who are more vulnerable to legal inquisitions. They also fear that concern over protecting and improving human heredity may divert attention from the pressing task of insuring social justice. Finally, they accuse eugenicists, or some of them at least, of having confused *biological* superiority with *economic* superiority. They say that genetics has openly called attention to the peril that confronts the species by virtue of the high rate of reproduction among the lower classes in contrast to the higher classes. But, in truth, nothing is more uncertain than the genetic effect of this "differential fecundity." Any comparison as to degrees of success is obviously vitiated from the outset by glaring inequalities with respect to the educational and economic circumstances that prevail in contemporary societies; furthermore—as Wettstein[11] emphasized in a remarkable essay, "Palamedes"—in many instances success is not proof of personal worth but an indication of the absence of altruism and a feeling of belonging, a sign of excessive ambition or aggressiveness.

In spite of these superficial objections, we believe that the eugenic ideal is perfectly compatible with truly democratic aims. A just and sane ideal in itself, it will be better understood, accepted, and adopted if presented to a more egalitarian and humane society. It is to be hoped that henceforth the ideal will win new converts even if it is not incorporated into our legal codes.

One final question is posed concerning heredity.

Is it possible to improve and advance heredity by bringing about favorable mutations in the genetic endowment?

Theoretically, this does not seem wholly impossible since we now know how to use certain artificial agents (X-rays, ultraviolet rays, phenol, sulfa drugs, urethane, mustard gas, etc.) to bring about mutations in both plants and animals.

In the first place, however, most mutations produced in this way (if not all of them) are inferior to normal specimens; and in the second place, using the techniques now known, we are unable to obtain *at will* a particular mutation. Although we are certain that we can modify the hereditary substance and provoke genetic changes, we are nevertheless completely incapable of predicting the direction these changes will take. It is hardly necessary to add that under these circumstances we cannot even consider experimenting with the genetic endowment of human beings.

Another possibility has been unfolding in recent years: the adjunction of a third complete set of chromosomes to the diploid set carried by every normal specimen.

In plants and even in animals—frogs, toads, salamanders—it is possible, and even relatively easy, by subjecting a fertilized egg to certain conditions (for instance, to heating or cooling), to cause reduplication of the *maternal* chromosomes. The new specimens will have *three complete sets of chromosomes,* two from the mother and one from the father. Quite recently, results along this line have been obtained on mice and rabbits (Fischbert and Beatty, Häggqvist and Bane).

At the present time we do not know all the consequences of the adjunction of a supplementary set of chromosomes. If they should prove to be favorable, we might hope to use them for the benefit of our species, but with all the discretion and all the reserve imposed by such a momentous innovation in the field of human heredity.

SELECTED READING LIST

Alexander, Peter, *Atomic Radiation and Life.* Penguin Books Inc., Baltimore, 1957.

Boyd, William C., *Genetics and the Races of Man.* Little, Brown and Co., New York, 1950.

Butler, J. A. V., *Inside the Living Cell.* Basic Books, Inc., New York, 1959.

Dunn, L. C., and Dobzhansky, Th., *Heredity, Race and Society,* revised ed. New American Library, New York, 1952.

Glueck, Sheldon and Eleanor, *Physique and Delinquency.* Harper & Brothers, New York, 1956.

Haldane, J. B. S., *Heredity and Politics.* W. W. Norton & Co., Inc., New York, 1938.

Huxley, Julian, *Heredity East and West.* Abelard-Schuman Ltd., New York, 1949.

Kallmann, Franz J., *Heredity in Health and Mental Disorder.* Norton & Co., Inc., New York, 1953.

Lawler, S. D., and Lawler, L. J., *Human Blood Groups and Inheritance.* Harvard University Press, Cambridge, 1957.

McElroy, William, and Glass, Bentley, (editors), *The Chemical Basis of Heredity.* The Johns Hopkins Press, Baltimore, 1957.

Meier, Richard L., *Modern Science and the Human Fertility Problem.* John Wiley & Sons, Inc., New York, 1959.

Montague, Ashley, *Human Heredity*. The World Publishing Co., New York, 1959.

Morgan, Thomas Hunt, *Evolution and Genetics*. Princeton University Press, Princeton, 1925.

Muller, H. J., Little, C. C., and Snyder, L. H., *Genetics, Medicine, and Man*. Cornell University Press, Ithaca, 1947.

Neel, James V., and Schull, William J., *Human Heredity*. University of Chicago Press, Chicago, 1954.

Newman, H. H., *Multiple Human Births*. Doubleday, Doran & Co., Inc., New York, 1940.

Newman, H. H., Freeman, F. N., and Holzinger, K. J., *Twins: A Study of Heredity and Environment*. University of Chicago Press, Chicago, 1954.

Osborn, Frederick, *Preface to Eugenics*, revised ed. Harper & Brothers, New York, 1951.

Pauling, Linus, *No More War!* Dodd, Mead & Co., New York, 1958.

Rife, David C., *Dice of Destiny*, 2nd ed. College Book Co., Columbus, Ohio, 1947.

Snyder, Laurence H., *The Principles of Heredity*, 3rd ed. D. C. Heath and Company, Boston, 1946.

UNESCO, *The Race Concept*. UNESCO, Paris, 1952.

Wiener, A. S., and Wexler, I. B., *Heredity of the Blood Groups*. Grune & Stratton, Inc., New York, 1958.

Zirkle, C., (editor), *Death of a Science in Russia*. University of Pennsylvania Press, Philadelphia, 1949.

Notes to Chapter I

1. See J. A. V. Butler, *Inside the Living Cell* (New York, 1959).

2. Twins occur on the average once in 80 births. Identical twins are three times rarer than fraternal twins. Both types apparently depend on hereditary factors. The percentage of identical twins seems to increase somewhat with syphilitic infection. Cf. H. H. Newman, *Multiple Human Births* (New York, 1940); and H. H. Newman, F. N. Freeman, and K. J. Holzinger, *Twins: A Study of Heredity and Environment* (Chicago, 1954).

3. The same rare anomaly is sometimes found in both identical twins: congenital dilation of the kidneys and the ureters, congenital cerebral hernia of the occipital region, etc.

4. In identical twins, according to Turpin, the type, central design, details, and orientation of the fingerprint is the same; only the study of gaps and junctures will permit differentiation.

Notes to Chapter II

1. According to Penrose, the number of Mongolians is generally 0.3% of the population. Mongolism is characterized by a peculiar facial expression (widening and protuberance of the middle region of the face,

drooping eyelids, etc.) as well as by anomalies affecting the nervous system and endocrine glands.

2. The average age of mothers of Mongolian idiots is 37, rather than 29.

3. J. B. S. Haldane, *Heredity and Politics* (New York, 1938).

NOTES TO CHAPTER III

1. The spermatozoon consists almost wholly of a nucleus; the ovule, on the other hand, has around its nucleus a mass of *cytoplasm*.

2. It has recently been established that there are only forty-six chromosomes, or twenty-three pairs, in each zygote. (Translator)

3. See Laurence H. Snyder, *The Principles of Heredity* (Boston, 1946), pp. 342-355.

4. The exact manner of duplication has not yet been determined. See below, note 10. (Translator.)

5. See David C. Rife, *Dice of Destiny*, 2nd ed. (Columbus, Ohio, 1947).

6. It is not necessary to assume that the particles contained in one and the same chromosome are autonomous and completely independent of each other; some biologists envision a chromosome as a continuum with properties that differ according to the level being considered.

7. For exceptions to this rule see Chapter IX, "Sex-Linked Factors in Heredity."

8. Named for Johann Mendel, a monk who first discovered (1865) the basic mechanism of heredity through his admirable experiments with peas.

9. Substance that results from the combination of

a protein and a nucleic acid containing a sugar called deoxyribose. See William McElroy and Bentley Glass, *The Chemical Basis of Heredity* (Baltimore, 1957).

10. The nucleic acid DNA (deoxyribonucleic acid) is now believed to provide the key to heredity. Each chromosome is thought to contain a double spiral of chains wound one around the other. As the cell divides, each chain chemically attracts enough other materials to create a new DNA structure identical to the original. Specific traits are determined by clusters of atoms at specific loci on the spiral. (Translator)

11. It is possible that the cytoplasm plays an important role in specific inheritance, but we have no positive data to support this view.

Note to Chapter IV

1. Heterozygous individuals with the same visible trait (*phenotype*) may have different hereditary constitutions (*genotypes*).

Note to Chapter V

1. See Chapters XII and XIII.

Notes to Chapter VI

1. Without entering into the details of the physiology of transfusions, we recall that individuals belonging to group O are *universal donors*, that is, they can supply anyone with blood since their blood cells

contain no agglutinogen and are agglutinated by no serum; inversely, they can receive blood only from their own group since their serum contains both agglutinins and clots the cells of A, B, and AB. Individuals in group AB are *universal recipients,* that is, they can receive blood from anyone since their serum contains no agglutinin and causes no cell to clot; inversely, they can supply blood only to individuals of their own group, for their cells have both agglutinogens and are agglutinated by serums A, B, and O. As for individuals in groups A and B, they can receive blood from others in their group and also in group O; they can supply blood to individuals in their own group and also to those in group AB. There have been attempts to relate blood types to different physiological characters (resistance or predisposition to certain disorders) or even to psychological characters, but nothing definite has yet been established. Cf. S. D. Lawler and L. J. Lawler, *Human Blood Groups and Inheritance* (Cambridge, 1957).

2. See Chapter XV.

3. See A. S. Wiener and I. B. Wexler, *Heredity of the Blood Groups* (New York, 1958); and James V. Neel and William J. Schull, *Human Heredity* (Chicago, 1954), pp. 318-330.

4. Unless a genetic mutation occurs in one of the parents, and this is extremely improbable.

NOTES TO CHAPTER VII

1. See p. 19. Rh-positive would correspond to the presence of the dominant gene D, Rh-negative to the presence of the recessive gene *d.*

2. Even after the child's recovery the Rh condition may entail serious consequences (retardation in his motor or intellectual development). We still do not understand all the facts about the matter.

3. The conclusiveness of proof obviously varies with the number of blood characters involved; one gene may conceivably undergo mutation, but not several.

Notes to Chapter VIII

1. See Laurence H. Snyder, *The Principles of Heredity,* third ed. (Boston, 1946), pp. 342-355; and Ashley Montague, *Human Heredity* (New York, 1959), pp. 45-47.

2. Or *heterosomes,* in contrast to non-sexual chromosomes, often called *autosomes.*

3. In reality there are always a few more boys than girls (5 per cent), and since intrauterine mortality is greater for males than for females, approximately 120 male gametes must be formed for every 100 female gametes. The near equality of the sexes at birth results therefore from two disturbing forces acting in opposite directions (excess of males at conception and preferential elimination of males before birth). The biological reasons for the surplus of males at conception are not known; it would seem that gametes with the Y chromosome are more likely to bring about fertilization than are gametes with the X chromosome.

4. According to M. E. Bernstein, there is probably a correlation between the tendency to produce boys and the virility of the father.

5. *Annals of Eugenics* 13: 156 (1946).

6. By way of corroboration we have, first, all the hereditary facts linked to sex chromosomes (see below), showing that certain genes are carried in pairs by the female and individually by the male. Second, the existence of a chromosomal mechanism for determining sex has been irrefutably demonstrated in different vertebrates, notably salamanders, through the admirable experiments of the American biologist R. R. Humphrey, brilliantly completed by L. Gallien.

7. It has been proven that man has 23 pairs of chromosomes. See Montague, *op. cit.*, p. 30. (Translator.)

NOTE TO CHAPTER IX

1. See above (p. 46) the reservation that can be made concerning the existence of the Y chromosome.

NOTES TO CHAPTER X

1. This example is in part theoretical since it has not been established that the gene for red hair and the gene for the blood group are on the same chromosome.

2. It is even possible in the case of partial linkage to approximate the distance between the genes on the chromosome since the frequency of crossing over increases with the distance (see p. 19).

3. We have considered the case of the male carrier of the abnormal gene because the female crossing over, which amounts to nothing more than transfer-

ring the gene from one X chromosome to the other, can have no visible consequence. If the abnormal X or Y gene determines a recessive anomaly, genetic analysis becomes much more complicated even though the same principles are involved.

NOTES TO CHAPTER XI

1. The great chemist Michel-Eugène Chevreul died at the age of 103, his father at 91, and his mother at 93.

2. When several genes determine a character, each gene may have a special role or all may have the same role.

3. If we call the gene for blackness *a* and the gene for whiteness *A*, the mulatto would produce two types of gametes, each carrying either *a* or *A;* two mulattoes would therefore make possible four different combinations—*aa* (black), *aA* (mulatto), *Aa* (mulatto), and *AA* (white).

4. It is thought that superior individuals have cerebral hemispheres that are markedly asymmetrical (predominance of the right hemisphere in the left-handed individual and predominance of the left in the right-handed individual). This anatomical peculiarity is certainly congenital and is probably of genetic origin.

5. The correlation between the mentalities of children and parents is lower for foster parents than for true parents. A. M. Leahy, "Nature-Nurture and Intelligence," *Genet. Psychol. Monogr.*, IV (1935), 236-308.

6. Cf. Sheldon and Eleanor Glueck, *Physique and Delinquency* (New York, 1956).

NOTES TO CHAPTER XII

1. Genes borne on the nonhomologous segments of the X-chromosome are generally called "sex-linked"; genes carried on the nonhomologous segments of the Y-chromosome are called "holandric"; and genes carried on the homologous segments of both chromosomes are termed "partially sex-linked." (Translator.)

2. As a general rule, at least, for *modifiers* can prevent the manifestation of a dominant gene.

3. If the frequency of the recessive gene is p in a population and that of the normal dominant gene $(1{-}p) = q$, the frequency of afflicted homozygotes is represented by p^2, that of heterozygotes by $2\,pq$, that of normal homozygotes by q^2. The rarer the gene, the higher the ratio of heterozygotes to defective homozygotes.

4. Incidence depends on the country. In France it is 0.87% (statistics for 1901-1910, comprising 3,047,183 marriages); in Germany, 0.59% (statistics for 1875-1899, comprising 5,922,439 marriages).

5. Since the proportion is much greater than that found by taking 1/10,000 as the average incidence of albinism, it would seem that the defect occurs less frequently than this, or that it can be determined by different genes.

NOTES TO CHAPTER XIII

1. For a list and brief descriptions of inherited disorders see Ashley Montague, *Human Heredity* (New York, 1959), pp. 326-346. See also H. J. Muller, C. C. Little, and L. H. Snyder, *Genetics, Medicine, and Man* (Ithaca, 1947).

2. Variation in expressivity and reduced penetrance are manifested by many other genes. For example, penetrance of the gene for diabetes is only 10% (the gene is expressed in only one-tenth of the individuals that have received it). Penetrance can vary from 100% (the gene is always expressed) to 1% (the gene is very rarely expressed). Instead of the terms penetrance and expressivity, Frazer Roberts prefers *degree* and *frequency of manifestation*.

3. At least this is true in guinea-pigs. Here in the same genetic strain the percentage of polydactyls is clearly less in the progenies of old females than in those of young females. In fowls polydactylism affects the left side more often than the right side.

4. This diversity of effects produced by a single gene reappears in many other cases: the same gene can determine polydactylism, obesity, and retinal lesions (Laurence-Moon-Biedl syndrome); the same gene can also determine arachnodactylism and dislocation of the crystalline lens, sebacious facial adenoma and visceral excrescences (*epiloia*), etc.

5. See above, note 1.

6. Such a case is not rare in medical genetics. Different genes with similar effects are designated by J. Carles as *isophane* genes. According to Gates, some-

times only one gene is involved—one which has changed places on the chromosome (*translocation*).

7. The anomaly is not so rare in reality as in theory, however, for its expressivity varies in a small number of heterozygous women (incomplete recessiveness of the gene).

8. In 1798 Goethe made some observations concerning Daltonism in a young student in Jena. Diderot speaks of a "M. Kleckenberg, a Dutch official who could not distinguish green from red" and also of an Amsterdam writer's son who could distinguish no intermediate shades: "How many experiments might be performed with these two extraordinary individuals. . . ." (*Elements of Physiology.*)

9. The hemophilic's blood coagulates more slowly than the blood of normal individuals (from 18 to 60 minutes instead of from 10 to 25); the condition is doubtlessly attributable to the absence of a clotting agent (plasmatic tryptase).

10. These hormones (*estradiol*) seem, in effect, to inhibit to a certain extent the manifestation of the gene; this has led to the use of hormones in treating hemophilia.

11. Named for the Dutch physician K. Pelger, who first described it (1928).

12. See H. Nachtsheim, "The Pelger-anomaly in man and rabbit," *Journal of Heredity*, May 1950.

13. The English physician had been so impressed as a youth by the sight of two chorea victims that he resolved to devote his life to the study of the malady.

14. See Franz J. Kallmann, *Heredity in Health and Mental Disorder* (New York, 1953).

NOTES TO CHAPTER XIV

1. In the case of a recessive gene, it is assumed that the frequency of mutation must be two or three times higher than the incidence of the defect (since two recessive genes are necessary for its occurrence).

2. Malady characterized by hypertrophy of the sebaceous glands and by the presence of neoformations in the brain, kidney, heart, etc.

3. We say deleterious because mutation almost always involves an unfavorable change.

4. It is still too early even to approximate the genetic effects of atomic explosions. But see Peter Alexander, *Atomic Radiation and Life* (Baltimore, 1957); and Linus Pauling, *No More War!* (New York, 1958).

5. Out of ten stillborn children, three are victims of maternal syphilis; in contrast, miscarriages are rarely caused by syphilis. It has been held that the syphilitic microbe (treponema) can pass into the sex cells, but this is certainly untrue; moreover, we know of no infectious agent—with the possible exception of the virus (?) that causes cancer—that can be transmitted in the human species through the gametes.

NOTES TO CHAPTER XV

1. It will be recalled that identical twins owe their origin to the same random choice.

2. It can be assumed that as a rule the genes prevalent in a particular region are those appropriate

under existing environmental conditions to the survival of the individual.

3. These investigations, to be significant, must be directed toward indigenous populations modified to the least degree possible by immigration.

4. The blood factors actually do resist desiccation; this accounts for the fact that a "blood archeology" is now being developed. In the Egyptian mummies, the factors for A and B, both relatively common in present-day inhabitants of Egypt, have been identified. According to P. B. Candela (1938), it was possible to identify these factors in the fossil bones, and W. S. Laughlin (1949) believes that he has determined the blood group of a Tepexpan Man, about one thousand years old.

5. Serological classification, based on invisible traits in the human being, has the additional psychological advantage of having recourse to no criterion that might elicit irrational prejudices. The American anthropologist Boyd wryly points out that in certain parts of the world an individual is considered inferior if he has brown skin, but that nowhere is the possession of an *A* factor or an Rh-negative factor grounds for exclusion from the very best society. In short, classification according to blood is now *the least racial way of grouping men.*

6. Klineberg holds that there is *no difference* between races with respect to intelligence or adaptation. See UNESCO, *The Race Concept* (Paris, 1952).

7. William C. Boyd, *Genetics and the Races of Man* (New York, 1950); and L. C. Dunn and Th. Dobzhansky, *Heredity, Race and Society,* rev. ed. (New York, 1952).

NOTES TO CHAPTER XVI

1. The inheritance of mutilations is denied even by those who subscribe to the transmission of acquired characters. Everyone knows that a man who has accidentally lost a leg or an arm can produce normal children.

2. With respect to the transmission of acquired characters, the principal facts observed by Michurinists in the animal kingdom are said to concern blood characters transmitted *by the mother* following ablation of the spleen (Sakharoff's experiment). See Julian Huxley, *Heredity East and West* (New York, 1949); and C. Zirkle, ed., *Death of a Science in Russia* (Philadelphia, 1949).

3. It might be objected that hereditary diseases do exist and must have been acquired at some time or other, or else we would have to assume that primitive man had all of them, potentially at any rate, in his genetic endowment. It is true that they were acquired, but by the germinal substance—and this makes all the difference, for an acquired character is one acquired by the individual's body (or *soma*).

NOTES TO CHAPTER XVII

1. Not to mention "reverse selections" or "counterselections," brought about by wars, which eliminate the most robust and courageous individuals.

2. See Richard L. Meier, *Modern Science and the Human Fertility Problem* (New York, 1959).

3. The most readable account of the subject is

Frederick Osborn's *Preface to Eugenics* (New York, 1951).

4. See *Eugenics, Its Definition, Scope and Aims,* 1904.

5. Richet proposed a radical method of barring the weak from marriage: Have both partners swim across a wide stream, and allow no boat to come to the rescue of those swept away by the current.

6. The United States was the first to enact a sterilization law (Indiana, 1907).

7. The operation was first performed in 1814 by a Swedish surgeon; in 1897, Lenander began to popularize it.

8. Electro-coagulation at the point where the tubes join the uterus is also practiced.

9. This malady, which inevitably entails death at an early age, depends on a recessive gene (see p. 77). Parents who have produced an afflicted child *know* that both of them are carriers, and that they therefore have *one chance in four* of producing another condemned child.

10. See p. 65.

11. *American Naturalist,* 1933.

INDEX